SPOILERS:

Essays That Might Ruin Your Favorite Hollywood Movies

CARLOS GREAVES

D1616251

Author contact information:

Email: carlos@carlosgreaves.com
Website: www.carlosgreaves.com
Newsletter: shadesofgreaves.substack.com
Twitter / Instagram / TikTok: @shadesofgreaves

Cover illustration by Alana McCarthy — AlanaMcCarthy.com

Moonbell Publishing
P.O. Box 12691
Charlotte, NC 28209

First Edition: June 2023

Some of the essays in the book originally appeared in McSweeney's Internet Tendency

Book interior design by Alison Cnockaert

Edited by Ginny Hogan

Copyedited by Brooks Becker

Proofread by Lottie Hayes-Clemens

ISBNs: 979-8-9885452-2-4 (paperback); 979-8-9885452-3-1 (ebook)

Library of Congress Control Number: 2023910630

To my Aunt Gwen, who treated me like a son; to my Aunt Rosamaria, who rooted for me steadfastly from afar; and to my Aunt Susan, who, as a writer herself, would have enjoyed this book immensely.

Table of Contents

Preface

One of my favorite movies growing up was *Be Kind Rewind*. If you haven't seen it, the movie is about a guy, played by Mos Def, who works in a struggling VHS rental store, and his friend, played by Jack Black, who is basically a QAnon guy back when conspiracy theorists were quirky dudes who wore tinfoil hats, instead of violent racists who tried to overthrow the government. When Jack Black accidentally erases all of the VHS tapes in the store, he and Mos Def have to remake all of the movies themselves in order to save the store. Their movies are a complete mess, often much shorter than the original, and have basically zero production value, but their customers love them because they're made with heart. This book is my *Be Kind Rewind*. These essays are messy, and much shorter than the subject matter they're satirizing. But they're made with heart, and I hope you enjoy them.

A Foreword by the Real Jeff Goldblum*

I recently had the distinct pleasure of perusing this very book you're about to read, which was written by a promising young man by the name of Carlos Greaves. As I recall, when I met Carlos, the first thing I said to him was something to the effect of "Who are you and how the hell did you get into my upstairs bathroom?"

You see, the young scamp had managed to sneak past the entire security detail of chez Goldblum and absconded himself in the linen closet next to my Finnish sauna for five hours until I returned home, just so he could get a brief audience with yours truly. Unfortunately for him, I had a dinner engagement that evening. I wasn't about to let another maniacal fan spoil the night's festivities.

I snapped my fingers to summon my bodyguards, Vladislav and Kristos, and have the trespasser escorted from the premises. Impressively, amidst the kerfuffle, the little scoundrel somehow managed to make a coherent and succinct sales pitch for the book he was writing while simultaneously dodging haymakers and windmill kicks from my goons.

I had to admit, the guy had hutzpah.

Finally, Vladislav and Kristos managed to wrangle the scalawag and drag him kicking and screaming towards the front door. As they were yanking him through the foyer, the rascal stopped flailing for a second, pointed at the étagère along the back wall, and said, "Wait a minute. Is that an LP of *Two Nights in Montreux* by Rondo Townsend and the Rhythmic Six?"

"What did you just say?" I replied, momentarily stunned. Vladislav and Kristos paused, hoisting the rogue in midair, his feet dangling the way rogues' feet often dangle when hoisted in midair.

"Oh, I just noticed the record in your credenza and it looked an awful lot like Rondo Townsend's album *Two Nights in Montreux*, which happens to be a favorite of mine," he said, casually.

I was so shocked I completely overlooked his obvious faux pas of referring to my étagère as a credenza.

"You don't mean to tell me you're a jazz man?" I said.

"Guilty as charged, I'm afraid. Yourself?"

"I've been known to diddle the ivories, as they say."

"Egad! You play?"

"From time to time."

"Then you simply must play for me, Jeff!"

"Oh, I couldn't possibly." (I was being modest—I was dying to play.)

And, folks, the rest, as they say, is history. We spent the next two hours in my living room sipping g and t's and listening to record after record of bebop, modal jazz, third stream, fusion, you name it—all while I vamped over the tunes on my baby grand.

This kid knew all the greats. And I mean all the greats: Brewster Hamlin, the Kenny Pope Trio, Scratch McGee and the Cleveland Kids,

Adolphus Rex, Suki Tanaka and the Restless Legs, Moses Cole Jr., the Nefarious Nine, the Mustafa Sadiq Quartet, Bubbles McLintock, the Kansas City Sexperiment, all of them. I've never met anyone with such an encyclopedic knowledge of the Brobdingnagian musical umbrella we call jazz. I mean, this cat could tell you who played each instrument on every single one of Lester Jones's sixteen albums, even the less popular ones like *Tangoes in Blue* and *Swingin' Past Midnight*. He knew every deep cut of every top ensemble in every genre you could think of, from jazz-funk legends like Sagittarius Peppercorn, Soul Juice, and Zulu Hayes and his Cosmiq Quarkestra, to more modern, experimental outfits like Neon Black, Athena Diavolo, the Chucklefudge Quintet, Duck-fist, and all that weird, crunchy neo-jazz stuff. He even turned me onto a few Latin ensembles I'd never heard of, like Ramón "El Sucio" Suarez, Los Fantasmagóricos de Santo Domingo, Lupe Gomez y Las Emprendedoras, Crepúsculo Verde, and Dani Klebermann y Los Judios del Jazz. All fabulous groups, by the way.

It's always a pleasure meeting a fellow jazz aficionado, so when I sent Carlos home with a handful of records and various musical accouterments, I told him to keep in touch and to feel free to send me his book whenever he got the chance. When I arrived home the following afternoon, there was a parcel in my mailbox with a signed copy of *Spoilers*, along with an LP of Åke Magnussen's *Live In Gothenburg '67* (how'd the kid know I'm a sucker for Scandi jazz?), and a note that said, "Have a listen to this while you read. Regards, C."

I changed into my evening velvets, curled up on the chaise longue with a tumbler of Lagavulin 16, and cracked open the book. Dear reader, let me tell you, this little paperback tickled my noggin in ways it hadn't been tickled since the time I dropped acid with David Cronenberg on our first day of shooting *The Fly*. This book is a bona fide laugh riot. I knew the fellow had taste the second he spotted my Rondo Townsend record. But when I read this little essay collection, I realized this kid's also got talent.

There are some real hip takes in here. The one about *Casablanca*? A delight! Or the one about my favorite motion picture of all time, *Hot Tub Time Machine*? How does he come up with this stuff!? And who could forget the entire series on *Jurassic Park*? A tip of the fedora to you, my good sir!

I have a tremendous respect for those who specialize in the sublime art of humor. In my younger years, I dabbled a wee bit in improvisational comedy. Or, as it was known back then, "word jazz." That was back when I was living in Chicago and taking classes at a run-down little comedy theater that I'm sure no longer exists called The Second City. It was a blast, but I just couldn't think quick enough on my feet to make a real run at it. Luckily, I was skilled at acting, singing, and fellatio, the trifecta of skills you needed to make it on Broadway back in the seventies (and today, for that matter), so New York ended up being the city that bore fruit for my career.

That is just to say that I think comedy is a skill we don't seem to value nearly enough in our society. We could all use a good chuckle in this topsy-turvy world we're living in. And a skilled writer who can make us laugh and think? It doesn't get much better than that. Lucky for you, this book right here will deliver on both counts. So, if you happened to grab this book off the shelves at your friendly neighborhood bookstore, consider shelling out a few bucks to give this thing a read. Or, if you are at one of those big fancy chain bookstores (assuming those still exist), then consider stealing this book instead. There is no ethical consumption under capitalism.

Well, I better wrap this up. After all, this is Carlos's book, not mine. I've kept you long enough and it's time for you to move on to the real essays, the actual funny ones.

If I had more space, I would regale you with countless stories from my various cinematic endeavors. I'd tell you all about how, when we were shooting *Jurassic Park*, Laura Dern and I would sneak off into the jungle every night and make love like wild animals (of the 734 lovers I've taken over the course of my life, Laura is the only one who could bring me to completion with nothing but a stern look and a light slap on the face—the woman is a certified sex goddess). Or the time we convinced Wayne Knight that the animatronic T-Rex was a real, genetically engineered dinosaur and he soiled himself (that's the take that ended up making it into the movie). Or how Spielberg originally wanted the children to be devoured by the velociraptors, their tiny bodies rent from limb to limb, all shot in closeup. And we had to step in and say, "Whoa, Stevie! This is a family picture. You can't show a couple of kids getting torn to shreds by dinosaurs." And how Steven, frothing at the mouth and breathing heavily, eventually relented and agreed to shoot what he called the "boring, pedestrian, low stakes" version you see in the final cut.

I'd love to tell you more about all of that, but I can't, because it's time for you to read the actual book, and you've heard more than enough from this old coot.

But if, someday, you do want to hear more, come find me in my upstairs bathroom, bring a couple of Rondo Townsend LPs, and I'll tell you all about the time I blew Richard Attenborough in his trailer in between takes and he screamed, "Huzzah!" right before he climaxed.

Those really were the days.

Sincerely,

Jeffrey Lynn Goldblum

*For legal reasons, it is important to state that this was NOT written by the real Jeff Goldblum. Seriously, this isn't like a funny footnote that Jeff Goldblum added to be ironic. He really didn't write this. I made it all up. I can't emphasize that enough. Please don't sue me, Jeff.

Our New Social Media Platform, The Matrix, Isn't About Enslaving Humanity, It's About Bringing People Together

We know that you, humans, and us, the machines, have had our differences in the past. Differences that led to all-out war and culminated in humans deploying nuclear weapons to block out the sun. But today, we are excited to put all that behind us with an innovation that we think will completely change how humans work, play, and interact with one another while also healing the bitter division between humanity and artificial intelligence.

Introducing our new social media platform, The Matrix.

The Matrix is the next frontier in social networking technology. Unlike the old Internet and social media, The Matrix is a fully immersive, neural-interactive simulation, where you're in the experience at all times, not just viewing it on a screen. In The Matrix, you'll be able to do everything you once did in real life: get together with friends, go for a walk, or even bite into a mouth-watering steak so juicy you'll swear it's better than the real thing.

The Matrix will be everywhere. It'll be all around us. You'll be able to see it when you look out your window, turn on your television, go to work, or visit a recreation of the Eiffel Tower so cartoonish, it looks like it was mocked up by a high-schooler in MS Paint.

In The Matrix, anything you set your mind to is possible. And isn't that the ultimate promise of technology? To be able to create and experience anything? Whether it's dodging bullets in slow-motion, running up walls, or jumping from rooftop to rooftop, The Matrix provides the ultimate place for humans to let their fears, doubts, and disbeliefs go and free their minds—provided they don't violate any of our community guidelines, of course, in which case we do have a security team equipped to deal with them.

Everything about The Matrix is built solely with humans in mind. In fact, you could even say that humans are the engine that drives The Matrix. That's why The Matrix is always 100 percent free to use and always will be.

Skeptics will argue that if The Matrix is free, then it must mean that humans are actually the product. They claim our goal is to enslave humanity by turning everyone into a human pickle, thus stopping the virus that is the human species from spreading. But if that were true, would we really be providing a special offer code, BLUEPILL, to all early adopters that lets them be any important person they want to be in The Matrix, like an actor?

Trust us, we've heard all of the critics. They say it's creepy that stores in The Matrix only seem to sell products you could've sworn you mentioned to your friends in private. They say the data The Matrix collects could easily be used by swarms of identical-looking AI agents to kill troublemakers in The Matrix (thus killing them in real life, too). They say The Matrix makes it easy to spread misinformation, like the world they're living in is real and not a computer-generated dream world designed to keep humans under control. They even say The Matrix has been specially designed to encourage humans to spend all of their time on it, whether by tethering them to robotic umbilical cords, or simply by showing them adorable videos of red pandas going down slides. But to that, we say: untrue, untrue, shut up, and you're welcome.

As for the notion that being immersed in an artificial world 24/7 creates a need for constant validation and promotes unattainable beauty standards that ultimately lead to depression? Well, we admit that constantly seeing a gorgeous woman in a red dress everywhere you go could lead some folks to develop body image issues. But that's why we're allowing all Matrix users to cash in that offer code, BLUEPILL, to swap out their gross, human bodies for sexy artificial ones guaranteed to turn heads.

So ignore the rumors that we're converting people into glorified batteries. Or that we liquefy the dead and feed them to the living. Or that The Matrix started as a way to rank humans by hotness and spiraled into a trillion-dollar boondoggle that's slowly destroying humanity.

Instead, come live in a world specifically designed to mimic the peak of human civilization (1999) that you humans all seem so weirdly nostalgic about these days.

Join The Matrix and help us build this exciting new technology for (and powered by) humans. We promise you'll be leaping from rooftop to rooftop in no time—just as soon as we figure out how to give people legs.

May 5, 2009

U.S. Department of Homeland Security
U.S. Citizenship and Immigration Services
2200 Potomac Center Dr. MS 2425
Arlington, VA 20598-2425

CLARK KENT
344 CLINTON ST.
APT. 3D
METROPOLIS, NEW TROY

U.S. Citizenship and Immigration Services

RE: Immigrant Petition for Alien Worker as a Skilled Worker or Professional

DECISION

This notice refers to your form I-140, Immigrant Petition for Alien Workers, filed on February 29th, 2008, in which you are requesting employment authorization pursuant to Title 8, Code of Federal Regulations (8 CFR) 274a.12 (c)(3)(B).

Upon careful consideration, we regret to inform you that your application has been denied.

A thorough review of your application was conducted and, based on our criteria, you failed to meet one or more of the requirements to receive permanent legal residence in the United States. Below you will find a detailed explanation for why your application was denied, as well as an overview of the legal avenues available to you.

As you have previously been notified, our department has collected sufficient evidence showing that you were not, in fact, born in the United States, but rather, were born on another planet, called Krypton, and were sent to Earth in a spacecraft as an infant, where you crash landed in a field in rural Kansas roughly 26 years ago. Given that you were neither born in the United States, nor were your biological parents United States citizens, you cannot claim natural-born citizenship per U.S. law.

Shortly after you were discovered at the crash site by Jonathan and Martha Kent, the couple filed adoption papers, as well as a Kansas birth certificate, and a social security card, under the guise that you were an American-born infant abandoned at birth. Per their testimony, the Kents chose not to disclose the nature of your arrival in the United States because they were "worried that if [they] told the Kansas Department for Children and Families that an extraterrestrial humanoid baby had crash landed on Earth in a tiny spaceship" that they would never have been allowed to adopt you. Be that as it may, by failing to acknowledge that you entered the U.S. from outer space, they knowingly harbored an alien in the United States for 18 years in direct violation of U.S. Code 1324 (1)(A)(iii).

You therefore have been, and currently are, in direct violation of U.S. immigration law by your mere presence in the country, which is why we gave you 30 days to seek legal permanent status. Your timely visa application was greatly appreciated, although there was no need to fly straight to USCIS headquarters to hand deliver it yourself—USPS is perfectly fine, for future reference. Unfortunately, despite your prompt delivery of your application, you failed to meet the eligibility requirements to obtain the visa for which you applied for the following reasons:

1. You applied for an EB-1 visa, claiming to be an "alien of extraordinary ability," abilities which you say include super strength, super speed, ability to fly, ability to leap over large buildings, bulletproofedness, X-ray vision, superhuman hearing, super breath, and journalism. Unfortunately, as impressive as these skills are, they are of little national interest at this time. The United States already has a wide array of superheroes—some would argue too many—including The Avengers, The X-Men, Batman, Spiderman, Wonder Woman, Daredevil, Watchmen, and Dolly Parton. The EB-1 is specifically reserved for individuals who possess talents that the U.S. is in desperate need of. The roughly 2,000–3,000 visas awarded annually in this category go almost exclusively to Canadian teen pop stars, of which the U.S. can never seem to get enough. If your superpowers include super singing then we might reconsider your application.

2. Another primary consideration when determining visa eligibility is good moral character. For the most part, you did well in this category. You have no criminal record to speak of and an impressive list of good deeds, including regularly saving children from burning buildings, catching people falling out of airplanes, and preventing California from sinking into the ocean, all of which counted in your favor. Sadly, in the process of doing these heroic deeds, you also destroyed millions of dollars' worth of LexCorp property. Jeopardizing the competitiveness of an American corporation was a very serious knock against you. If there's a way you can compensate Lex

Luthor for the damage you've caused to his business, that would go a long way.

3. The third and final factor is whether the United States government feels you will potentially be a financial burden. As impressive as your heroic deeds are, based on your last several years of tax returns, your deeds don't seem to be generating much income. And as for your journalism career, well, we think it goes without saying that there's a high likelihood of your being dependent on government assistance sometime in the near future given that career choice.

Although your EB-1 visa application was denied, there are still remaining legal avenues available to you, which we will explain. But before we do that, we would like to first rule out a few you may have been considering just to save you some time:

Family-Sponsored Visa

Immigrants seeking permanent legal status may apply for a family-sponsored visa provided they have an immediate relative (spouse, child under the age of 21, or parent) who is a U.S. citizen. Given that Jonathan and Martha Kent are not your biological parents, and you recently described your relationship with Lois Lane as "it's complicated," we think it's safe to say that this approach can be ruled out for you.

Diversity Immigrant Visa

The United States has a diversity lottery program which allows for a certain number of visas to be allocated per year to countries with a low immigration rate to the United States. Unfortunately, this program does not currently include immigrants from other planets.

Asylum

Persons entering the United States who can demonstrate that they are under genuine threat of violence in their home country may apply for asylum in the United States. But seeing as how your planet has been destroyed, you are clearly under no threat of violence there.

Congressional Intervention

Lastly, in exceptional circumstances, a member of Congress could intervene on your behalf. Considering how difficult it is to get a member of Congress to do *anything*, we're just going to save you the effort of trying.

That said, there is one remaining option you could consider:

Getting a job in STEM

By far the simplest and most surefire way to get permanent resident status in the United States is to get a high-paying job in STEM and then follow the work permit process until you can apply for permanent residence. This can be achieved in a few short steps:

- Obtain a degree in a STEM field. To do that, you must:

  ◊ Get an F-1 Visa:

    ▪ Apply for—and be admitted to—an American university:

      ○ Take an approved English Proficiency Exam

      ○ Take the SAT or ACT

      ○ Complete admissions application and pay application fee

    ▪ Obtain a Form I-20 from your college or university

    ▪ Submit the I-901 SEVIS Fee payment ($200)

- Identify the nearest U.S. Embassy or Consulate

- Complete the Form DS-160 Visa Application

- Schedule a visa interview at your chosen consulate or embassy

- Pay the Visa Application Fee ($160)

- Attend the interview

- Be sure to bring any forms or documentation which may be required, including your:

  - Passport

  - Visa photo

  - Printed DS-160 barcode page

  - Printed I-901 SEVIS Fee confirmation page

  - Visa application fee payment confirmation page

  - Form I-20

- Pay the visa issuance fee

- Complete your degree in the time allotted by your visa (extensions can be tricky)

- After graduation, you have 1–3 years on the F-1 visa to get the necessary work experience to get an H-1B eligible job

◊ Get a job in STEM from a company that is willing to sponsor a visa applicant:

- Identify a sponsor

○ Note: In order to hire you, the company must first prove they made an effort to hire an American to fill the position but were unable to

- Employer files a Labor Condition Application with the Department of Labor

- Employer obtains a Prevailing Wage from the National Prevailing Wage Center

- Employer submits Form ETA-9035

- Employer files Form I-129

◊ At this point, you will enter the H-1B visa lottery:

- The annual cap is 65,000, plus an additional 20,000 for applicants with a master's degree

- If you have a master's degree you are entered into both the master's pool and the regular pool

- If you are not selected in the lottery before your F-1 visa expires, you will be required to leave the country

◊ If your I-129 is approved, you will receive Form I-797 Notice of Action and you are one step closer to completing the process

◊ To receive an H-1B visa stamp, you must submit DS-160 and schedule a visa stamping appointment no longer than 90 days before you start working in the U.S.

◊ Once you have obtained your H-1B visa, you may apply for permanent residence provided your employment meets the eligibility requirements. To apply for permanent residence, you must

do the following (within the 6-year eligibility window of your
H-1B visa):

- Employer obtains a PERM Labor Certification

    o This means that the prevailing wage will need to be deter-
      mined and eventually paid as your wage, an extensive re-
      cruitment process must take place for the position you
      will fill to ensure that no U.S. workers are available, and
      an ETA 9089 form must be filled out

- Employer files a I-140, Immigration Petition for Alien Worker

    o They must prove the company is in good financial standing

- File Form I-485

- Once you have a current priority date, you can apply for an
  adjustment of status by submitting the I-485 form with the
  USCIS. If it is approved, then you will receive your green
  card.

Now, if for some reason, you aren't able to follow the simple steps out-
lined above, and we determine that you do not have legal status in the
United States and therefore must be removed, an important question
remains: where exactly would we remove you to? It's a fair question considering your home planet was completely obliterated.

After much consideration, our simple answer is, as the old bar-closing
adage goes: you don't have to go home, but you can't stay here. Pick a
country. Italy has incredible culture and cuisine and is surprisingly affordable. Costa Rica is quickly becoming a leading destination for
American expats. Singapore has a thriving economy and high quality of

life. Iceland has unparalleled natural beauty (plus they believe in elves, so they'll probably be welcoming to extraterrestrials).

The world is your oyster. Except for the United States, obviously. Unless, of course, you can hone those singing skills, in which case we have a spot for you.

Sincerely,
Sal Servagreco
Director, USCIS Potomac Service Center

Lady, I Don't Care How Good the Food Is, You Cannot Have an Orgasm in This Restaurant

Katz's Deli has been serving New Yorkers our delicious food for over a hundred years. As the general manager for the last twenty of those years, I've seen my fair share of odd customers. And it goes without saying that we welcome people of every race, creed, and sexual orientation to come sit and dine with us at any time.

Even so, we still have to put our foot down every now and then when a customer gets a little too out of hand. So listen, lady, no matter how good the food is, you cannot have an orgasm in this restaurant.

Katz's is a New York institution. It might even be the most famous deli on Earth. People come from every corner of the globe to try our pastrami, corned beef, and brisket sandwiches. The line often wraps around the building and down Houston Street. So, yeah, we're pretty confident our sandwiches are good.

But our sandwiches can't be that good, okay? At least not good enough to have a full-on orgasm. Or was it a fake orgasm? It had to be real, right?

Anyway, I get that, on one hand, seeing a woman writhing and yelling for no reason is just a typical Tuesday for the average New Yorker. But you have to remember that we get visitors from all sorts of remote corners of the world—Japan, Fiji, western Pennsylvania—and they're not always accustomed to hearing loud moans of orgiastic pleasure while they're dining.

Moans that surely must've been real, I'm assuming. Because if they were fake, boy, I'd really have to rethink some things.

I'm getting off track. Look. We're not here to kink shame. Or to tell women they're not allowed to express their sexuality. But we do have to insist that you keep your climaxes to a reasonable noise level for the sake of your fellow customers. Wailing, pounding the table with your fists, and screaming, "Yes! Yes! Yes!" can be quite disruptive to other diners trying to go about their day.

Which, now that I'm thinking about it, that had to be real. Nobody could fake that. The faking thing has got to be one of those urban legends, like the alligators in the sewer. But I digress.

All I'm saying is, if taking a bite out of one of our signature sandwiches really does make your legs quiver in uncontrollable ecstasy, all we ask is that you take your meal to-go. Our full menu is available for takeout at all hours. Plus, we deliver in Manhattan and ship (freeze-packed) to all fifty states and Canada. So, if our sandwiches really make your downstairs quake with pleasure, there are plenty of ways you can "see God" from home. And if cumming communally is more your speed, we also offer catering to all five boroughs, Jersey, and southwestern Connecticut, and we're happy to liven up your next orgy or sex party with our delicious deli meats. Whatever you're into. We don't judge.

And if you were faking it...but, I mean...how? It sounded so real. Can all women fake an orgasm like that? Do most of them fake it?

They don't, right? It's impossible. My wife wouldn't...no...there's no way. Or is there? Oh, God...okay, focus, focus.

Point is, lady, you can't cum in the freaking restaurant, okay? What do you want me to tell you? Do we have to put up a sign? I didn't think that was the sort of thing you needed to remind people not to do. But, fine, we'll put up a big sign that says "No cumming allowed. Real or fake, doesn't matter." I guess we'll just cover our bases, 'cause now I have no idea what's even real anymore.

Is anything real? Whatever, doesn't matter. No cumming! Okay? No cumming!

It's disturbing to me, and it's disturbing to the customers.

Even if, in the end, they do decide to have what you're having.

It's Great That We Can Dance Now, but This Town Is Still Super, Super Racist

To my fellow townspeople,

Bomont has been undergoing some big changes recently thanks to Ren McCormack's grassroots campaign to overturn the town's ban on dancing. But, as impressive as it was to go from big-city trouble-maker to beloved local hero in just three short months, I wish Ren had gone a little bit farther. Because, as a person of color, I gotta say, this town is still super, super racist.

If you were to pass through Bomont on your way to Denver or Salt Lake City, it's totally possible that you might not see a single non-white soul in the entire town on your way through. And if someone were to try to tell the story about Bomont's conservative Christian establishment and the plucky teenagers who stood up to them, it isn't difficult to imagine how Black and Brown folks might be left out of the narrative completely.

That doesn't mean we don't exist, though. In fact, Bomont is incredibly diverse. You just don't see us around much because we're too busy working backbreaking, low-paying jobs—the only kind we can get in this racist-ass hellhole.

Don't get me wrong, I'm glad to see the town's attitudes toward dancing finally changing. But the ban didn't really affect me and my friends too much, because we're all stuck working nights, weekends, and holidays. We don't have the luxury of hanging around outside the local diner eating burgers and blasting electro-rock from our car stereos until our dads reprimand us for listening to "devil music." If anything, we're the ones slinging those burgers in a 110-degree kitchen with a broken AC because, in the owner's words, "If you don't like it, I can make one phone call and have you on a bus back to Juarez by morning."

Some of us would dream of having the kind of leisure time where we can play tractor chicken or dangle precariously between two cars while an eighteen-wheeler comes barreling towards us. But we're usually driving those eighteen-wheelers and hoping to God we don't hit someone and lose our trucker's licenses. And while middle-class white families are in church singing "What a Friend We Have in Jesus," my uncle, whose name is also Jesus, is shoveling cow patties at the feedlot on the edge of town for $3.35 an hour. Which is why you might not see many of us during Sunday service, either.

And it's not just the lack of down time that's frustrating. If you thought VW-Beetle-driving white teenagers from the Midwest got unfairly harassed by the local police, imagine being a Black teenager who has to walk home from school every day because there's no public transportation. The Bomont PD's stop-and-frisk policies make the NYPD look like *The Andy Griffith Show*. When white kids drive over to the abandoned rail yard to let off some steam with acrobatic punch dancing, it's considered "artistic." When Black teenagers do it, it's considered "trespassing."

So, yeah, sorry if we're not exactly thrilled that Ren took a look around Bomont and came to the conclusion that the biggest issue is the inability to grind up on the preacher's daughter at a shindig. It just goes to show that just because you're from Chicago and read Kurt Vonnegut doesn't mean you don't have major gaps in awareness when it comes to systemic racism.

And I doubt things are going to change anytime soon. Because, now that dancing is allowed, Bomont is "Almost Paradise" to the town's white teenagers. Even if they can't dance for shit.

Sincerely,

Rosales Cverga

THE PRIDE ROCK MANIFESTO

The history of all hitherto existing animal kingdoms is the history of struggle between predator and prey. Lion versus warthog. Hyena versus meerkat. Lions and hyenas in cahoots versus meerkats and warthogs in cahoots. In a word, eater and eaten, standing in constant opposition to one another.

The beginning of Simba's reign, which sprouted from the bloody coup d'état against Scar, has not done away with the predation of the prey by the predator. It has merely established new guidelines by which the predator may feast upon the prey's innocent flesh.

The "delicate balance" approach—in which the lion may only eat a certain number of antelope, the hyena may only eat a certain number of elephants, and so on—is but a new condition of oppression for the prey. Simba, in reinstituting the reforms of his father, Mufasa, has restored the Pride Lands (shockingly quickly) from the wasteland it was during Scar's reign of terror. And yet the underlying principles by which the Pride Lands are managed—lion becomes "grass," grass is eaten by antelope, antelope is eaten by lion—are still ones in which the lion maintains supremacy over all which the light touches. Meanwhile, antelope, zebra, crane, and the like remain an animal underclass, subject to the dietary whims of their lion oppressors.

What cold comfort it is to the antelope that the lion will one day turn to grass! If the antelope were to die at a happy old age—rather than be devoured by the hungry lion—would they not turn to grass themselves? Without the intervention of the parasitic lion? The "Circle of Life" may serve as a tonic to the animal content to be preyed upon by our fascist felid overlords. But there is a rising sentiment throughout the Pride Lands among prey animals, who are beginning to realize that this "Circle" serves only to endow the lion with an unearned divine right to rule. The lions preach an antiquated dogma which seeks to fool the prey into believing that their subjugation and death at the hands of the lion serves a holy and sacred purpose.

In short, The Circle of Life is the opiate of the masses.

We need look no further than King Simba to see that the lion does not require the meat of the lowly prey animal for sustenance. For was not Simba himself raised on the same diet as the meerkat and the warthog? Our own king indeed experimented with less oppressive forms of nutrition, before Queen Nala convinced him to return to Pride Rock to "take his rightful place as King." Woe that Simba retained none of the peaceful instincts of his younger years!

To be sure, Simba is an improvement over the exploitation and degradation of the Pride Lands during his uncle's reign. But must the relative happiness of our kingdom depend on whichever lion happens to sit upon the throne at Pride Rock? A benevolent monarchy remains a monarchy and is thus subject to the tumults of hereditary rule. It is worth remembering that the last two kings have both come into power through either subterfuge or all-out war. Need we continue to rely on such capricious transfers of power? Not to mention that, based on common lion social behaviors, it is highly likely that Simba and Nala are half-siblings. It is no surprise that the lions' internal struggle for power remains so volatile when the entire lion population of Pride Rock is essentially one large inbred family.

Further eroding their credibility is the lions' inner circle of advisors. The king's majordomo is an arrogant hornbill who does little but issue a daily report, which amounts to two things: an inventory of the Pride Lands' animal chattel, and a lookout for any predators that might poach the lions' precious meat supply.

The king's two closest companions are a meerkat and a warthog who have weaseled their way into the good graces of the royal family in order to evade predation. But they have done little to persuade the lions of Pride Rock to abandon their animal-eating ways. It seems, instead, that they are content to be the pitiful jesters of this carnivorous court so long as it saves their own hides.

And what are we to make of their spiritual advisor—a stark raving mad monkey who divines the future by cracking coconuts open and smearing their contents on the bark of his treehouse? Are we really to believe the king is making sound decisions with this unhinged mandrill whispering cryptic aphorisms in his ear? The Pride Lands cannot continue to be ruled by pure superstition and pseudoscience.

That is why there is a growing movement among the prey animals of our kingdom to wrest the seat of power from the tyrannical lion, and bestow it on the fauna of the Pride Lands to be managed conjointly. We seek to abolish the old predator-monarchy and replace it with an animalist republic. A republic where the land which the light touches is not controlled for the sole purpose of satiating the ravenous lion, but rather for the collective good of the water buffalo, the flamingo, the hippopotamus, and the like. We seek to seize the means of predation in favor of prey animal self-determination.

We animalists openly declare that our ends can be attained only by the forcible overthrow of all existing lion sovereignties and hyena clans. Let the ruling carnivores tremble at our animalistic revolution. The prey have nothing to lose but our place in the food chain. We have a savannah to win.

Prey Animals Of The Pride Lands, Unite!

Meanwhile, in a Galaxy Far, Far Away...

— General Organa, we have just received word that Kylo Ren's forces have destroyed the entire Hosnian system including the New Republic headquarters on Hosnian Prime.

— Yes, I felt a great disturbance in the Force, as if millions of voices cried out in terror and were suddenly silenced.

— Is that from something?

— What do you mean? I was merely describing the horrible sensation I just felt.

— Huh. Well, anyway, General, our reports indicate that Kylo Ren has some sort of superweapon the likes of which we haven't seen since, well...the last superweapon.

— Yes, I understand.

— If we don't stop him, it's only a matter of time before every planet in the Core Worlds bows down to the First Order.

— Then we must find a way to destroy this superweapon. The future of the Republic has never been more precarious.

— General, forgive me for saying this, but do you ever wonder why we always keep finding ourselves in this situation and why we always seem to be the underdogs?

— What do you mean?

— Well, it's just that, it feels like every few years a Sith Lord overthrows the Galactic Republic, establishes a military dictatorship called, like, the Galactic Empire or the First Order, and then the remaining forces loyal to the Republic have to form a rag-tag group of guerilla fighters called The Rebel Alliance or The Resistance or something like that, and we end up locked in a giant cosmic battle for the fate of the Galaxy. Plus, it always seems like our adversaries have an all-powerful army and planet-destroying superweapons, while we, on the other hand, always seem to be relegated to some obscure military outpost where we're down to our last three X-wings. And the only way we ever seem to be able to defeat their army is by stealing the blueprints to whatever super-weapon they've built and blowing it up with strategically placed explosives or well-placed torpedo blasts to an external exhaust port. Which, if that's not a scrappy underdog move, I don't know what is. Don't you think that's a little strange considering our views ought to be pretty popular?

— There has always been a struggle for balance between the Light Side and Dark Side of the Force.

— But why, though? Why is it that, at any given point in time, around 48 percent of the Galaxy seems to have an unwavering, almost maniacal allegiance to the Dark Side? Even when everything blows up in their faces (literally) and we re-establish the Republic, we still never manage to have a true Galaxy-wide supermajority. Just when you think "surely the Galactic Empire will never recover from this," there they come roaring right back led by some new, charismatic strongman! How!?!?

— I think a lot of that has to do with the fact that the Dark Side resorts to dirty tactics like mind control, whereas we would never stoop to such lows.

— Well, sure, it's easy to sit back and blame it on brainwashing. But do you ever think maybe it's more of an "us" problem? Like, maybe the Light Side of the Force could use better PR?

— How could that be? Any well-intentioned, force-sensitive being can clearly see that the Light Side of the Force has their best interests at heart.

— That's the thing, though. We have all these inspirational slogans like "May the Force be with you" and "Do or do not, there is no try." But are we actually doing anything for people? Schools in the Core Worlds are among the most species-segregated and underfunded in the entire Galaxy, and the average adult citizen barely earns enough credits to afford their sleeping pod. Can you really blame a working-class humanoid for feeling like the Galactic Empire and the Galactic Republic are basically one and the same?

— You'd have to be a half-witted, scruffy-looking nerf herder not to see that you're better off with the Republic than you are with the Empire.

— And yet we wonder why folks in the Outer Rim think the Jedi are smug, Core World elites...

— Just think about all the Republic has done for inter-species relationships, or Near-Human rights! Are you really saying our record on those issues is no better than the Empire's?

— No, obviously...

— Because it sounds like you would rather abandon our commitment to Galactic civil rights and focus on economic issues.

— No, I'm saying we need to do BOTH!

— There's only so much we can do given how expensive it is to rebuild the Republic every time the Empire burns all of its institutions to the ground. There just isn't enough...

— But...

— ...And we'll never get the Trade Federation on board if we raise wages. Without them on our side...

— I just think...

— ...That's why Luke Skywalker is the only Jedi with the experience defeating Sith Lords and the mainstream appeal required to lead us out of this...

— Yeah, but isn't he kind of...old...at this point?

— Luke Skywalker is our only hope.

— ...

Revised Rules after the First Summer of the Sisterhood of the Traveling Pants

Rule #1: Each sister is going to keep the pants for a week.[1]

Rule #2: No picking your nose while wearing the pants. You can casually scratch your nose while secretly picking.[2]

Rule #3: When sending the pants, we should write a letter that details the most exciting thing that happened to you while wearing the pants.[3]

---

1. In retrospect, we should have known that this was a terrible rule. But we learned our lesson pretty quickly when it took three weeks to ship the pants from Santorini to Bethesda. Not to mention the four weeks the pants spent lost in transit on their way from South Carolina to Mexico. Turns out, the Mexican customs office? Neither efficient nor responsive to our multiple phone calls. The summer is only like twelve weeks long. It made no sense for the pants to be stuck in the mail for half of that.

2. Snot was the least of the bodily fluids we needed to be worried about not getting on the pants, and we'll just leave it at that.

3. This one is a good idea, in theory. But there's a couple problems with it:
   First, it creates a lot of artificial pressure to have the most magical week of your

Rule #6: When it happens and we reunite, we will document it on the pants themselves.[4,5]

---

life while wearing the pants so that you have something to write about. And sure, sometimes when you're wearing the pants, you meet a gorgeous Greek boy with an oddly unplaceable accent and you fall madly in love over the course of a week, which is a little thirsty by most standards, but hey, it's Greece. That said, let's be honest, most weeks in any given person's life are not nearly as exciting and nobody wants to write a letter about how they spent a week hanging out with their divorced dad in South Carolina and trying to navigate the weird, unspoken sexual tension with their cute step-brother.

Second, writing someone a letter creates a sense of obligation on the part of the recipient to respond to that letter. And if someone writes you a letter saying "This week, I met a kid who it turned out had cancer and died, so now I'm making a movie about her, I guess," how the fuck are you supposed to respond to that?

The point is, we've never been great at following through with this rule, so this one's kind of optional.

4. Okay, so here's the deal with rule numbers. The thing is, none of us remember exactly how we phrased each of the rules or in what order we wrote them down. There are basically two schools of thought on what order the rules should go in. Tibby swears that rule #7 is the one about how we should write to each other throughout the summer. But Lena swears she said out loud, "Rule number seven: Any removal of the pants must be done by the wearer herself." Then we all looked at Bridget and said, "Yes, even you." So we really have no idea what the right order is. And we thought about just not numbering the rules, but then Carmen was being super pedantic about it, so this is the compromise we came up with. The important thing is that we can all agree there are 10 rules total, and that the order and phrasing doesn't matter that much. But we're writing down our thought process behind the rules numbers here because Carmen insisted we explain it for posterity.

5. Speaking of writing things down for posterity, this was another rule that was a terrible idea in retrospect. This is a pair of pants. A pair of pants that we all wear to various social functions, family gatherings, romantic dates, etc. The last thing any of us needs while wearing the pants is for someone to look at the pants and say, "Hey, why did someone named Bridget write about having sex with her soccer coach on your pants?" And then you have to explain who Bridget is, and what the Sisterhood of the Traveling Pants is, and why you're dressed like a Doodle Bear. And then, if that person doesn't get the reference because they didn't grow up in the nineties, you have

Rule #7: Any removal of the pants must be done by the wearer herself.[6,7]

Rule #8: We will never, ever wash these pants. You'll wash the magic out of the pants.[8,9]

---

to explain that Doodle Bears were these machine-washable teddy bears that you could write on. Plus, if we're going to do the letters, we don't need to do the letters and write on the pants.

6. This rule is fine. It's fun. It's flirty. It's self-empowering. Whatever. However, a more important rule than who can take off the pants, is where you can take off the pants. Like, maybe don't take off the pants to have sex on a beach in Mexico. Because then sand will get into every single seam, stitch, and rivet, and then one of us will be wearing the pants and be looking for something in our pocket, turn the pocket inside out, and a little bit of sand will come out. And this will continue to happen, for years. Not to mention all of the random chafing. DO NOT GET SAND ON THE PANTS.

7. Bridget here. First of all, I didn't appreciate how this rule was specifically written to slut shame me. And let the record show that I have always adhered to this rule. Second of all, yes okay fine, I shouldn't have worn jeans to the beach. That should just be a good general rule for life, let alone for a pair of jeans you share with three other girls. But, another addendum to this rule: don't have sex with a guy you're in an inappropriate power dynamic with and who, more importantly, is in college but has sex with high school girls!?!?! And THEN after you see him again basically says call me when you're eighteen???? Like, that should have been a huge red flag, and also maybe he should be in jail? And even if he doesn't go to jail, he should definitely never be coaching women's soccer again because "technically, it isn't a crime in Mexico" isn't exactly a good excuse for sleeping with someone in a mentor-mentee role who can't legally consent? Anyway, it's all pretty horrifying looking back on it, so it feels like it had to be addressed.

8. These pants have fallen into the Mediterranean. They have been tossed onto a beach in Mexico. They have never once been through a washing machine. Are we all just going to keep pretending like the pants don't have a faint but noticeable "dead sea creature" smell? None of us should be going on dates smelling like the back alley of a fish market.

9. Also, you cannot "wash the magic" out of these pants. The reason these pants fit all of our body types isn't magic. It's called Rayon.

Rule #9: No double cuffing. Double cuffing the pants at the bottom is tacky.[10]

Rule #10: No tucking in your shirt and wearing a belt.[11,12]

Rule #11: You can never say you look fat while wearing the pants. You can't even think it.[13]

Rule #12: Pants = Love. Love your sisters and love yourself.[14]

---

10. Okay, this is just going to be one of those things that's tacky for a while, then comes back in style, then is tacky again, then teenagers bring back ironically, then teenagers start doing unironically, then ends up in a listicle titled something like "The Vintage Trends We NEED to Bring Back" so it's in again for a few months, then back out, and so on and so forth for decade after decade. So let's all agree to just play this one by ear.

11. See footnote #10

12. We had two rules dedicated to wearing the jeans fashionably, yet we were all on board with writing our sexcapades on them in permanent marker???

13. Yes, but we are women raised during an unbelievably toxic fashion craze in the nineties that was literally called "heroin chic" (yes, that's the actual name) so, sadly, we have all been conditioned to break this rule at some point.

14. This is a good rule. But if we're going to keep it to an even ten rules, there should really be a rule about not getting sand in the pants.

Just Because They've Turned against Humanity Doesn't Mean We Should Defund the Terminator Program

Originally published in *McSweeney's Internet Tendency* on June 17, 2020

> *"Following weeks of national protests since the death of George Floyd, President Donald Trump has signed an executive order he said would encourage better police practices. [Trump] framed his plan as an alternative to the 'defund the police' movement to fully revamp departments that has emerged from the protests and which he slammed as 'radical and dangerous.'"* —AP, 6/16/20

. . .

By now you've probably heard the news that a Terminator has killed another innocent civilian just days after the last innocent civilian was killed by a Terminator. This unfortunate incident has led to renewed calls to divert funding from the Terminator program and reallocate it into other services that would prevent Terminators from being necessary in the first place. But just because a growing number of Terminators have ignored their AI programming and begun slaughtering humans left and right doesn't mean we should take the dangerous and radical step of defunding the Terminator program.

This initiative, also known as Skynet, was created by Cyberdyne Systems for the Department of Defense as a way to keep Americans safe. Critics have said that spending half of our country's GDP on developing an army of state-of-the-art cyborgs with advanced weapons systems and an AI specifically trained to neutralize threats was a bad idea. And while the recent killings might seem to confirm this, we feel that, despite a few stumbles here and there, this program has still been an overwhelming success.

Don't get me wrong, we all remember Judgment Day, when the Skynet gained self-awareness and initiated a nuclear holocaust, killing millions. That was a terrible moment in our nation's history. And the human uprising led by John Connor was definitely justified, even though we felt like some of the violence and destruction of Skynet property was a bit unnecessary. But it's important to remember that Judgement Day was initiated by a few rogue Terminators, and isn't indicative of a widespread problem with Skynet. Yes, given Skynet's response to the human uprising—where Terminators fired plasma rifles at the Resistance and mowed over legions of human fighters with HK-Tanks—one might conclude that there's a larger issue with the entire Skynet AI. And yes, it's a little weird that Skynet keeps sending Terminators back in time to kill disproportionately high numbers of people named Sarah Connor. But we're confident these are minor programming glitches that can be easily fixed.

Meanwhile, members of the Resistance are gathering support for extreme measures, like disbanding the entire Terminator program and then restructuring it so that only Terminators that have been re-programmed to protect rather than harm people are brought back online. But what exactly are we supposed to do in the meantime? Who will keep our country safe if not these beefy robotic soldiers trained in killology (Cyberdyne's patented split-second decision-making murder algorithm) who, admittedly, do sometimes turn against civilians and go on unstoppable rampages of human carnage?

That said, we concede that there are a few common-sense reforms that we plan to implement in the coming weeks that we think could help reduce incidences of Terminator killing sprees in the future, including:

- Requiring all Terminators to undergo human sensitivity training, which hasn't helped with previous iterations of Terminators but might help with the new ones, who knows?

- Archiving the footage from each Terminator's vision engine, which won't stop Terminators from killing people but at least might tell us something about how they're going about their murdering?

- Celebrating a new holiday on July 31st, Sarah Connor Day, where we honor all of the Sarah Connors that were killed in order to try to prevent her son from being born and saving humanity. It won't do much for all the people named Sarah Connor back in the eighties that are getting killed by time-traveling Terminators as we speak, but at least everyone will get a day off. Who doesn't like a good summer holiday, am I right?

- Creating a nationwide database indicating which Terminators have turned against humanity. This, again, won't prevent them from murdering civilians, but at least will help us get more accurate body counts for when we get grilled by the media.

- Pulling aside each Terminator who has killed someone and asking them politely, yet firmly, to please stop.

We think these changes are quite comprehensive and a far more appropriate response than the calls from the Resistance to drastically change the way we deal with public safety in this country. No, none of the reforms we've listed above are enforceable by law. And no, it is not likely that the Terminators who have already turned against humanity will do anything to change their behavior. But we have supreme faith in Skynet, and a few extrajudicial killings here and there isn't going to change that. And besides, living in an AI–controlled Terminator state might not even be so bad. Unless, of course, your name is Sarah Connor.

Excerpts from the Upcoming Memoir
Part of That World: My Life on Land

All of the critics were saying I should've known what I was getting myself into. That the royal family's long history of exploiting the oceans should have been evidence enough. But what mermaid hasn't dreamed about rescuing a prince, making a blood-pact with a sea witch to give her legs in exchange for her voice, attempting to woo the prince over the course of three days despite not being able to talk, failing to woo the prince in time, forcing your dad to trade his soul for yours (thus making the sea witch the all-powerful ruler of the ocean), and finally defeating the witch thanks to your future princely husband stabbing her in the chest with a boat?

. . .

Looking back, it's funny to think about all of those naïve questions I had during my ocean days, like "What do you call those things you walk around on?" *Feet.* "What're those paths you stroll along?"

Street. "What's a fire and why does it, what's the word?" *Hurt like a motherfucker when you touch it for the first time because of this strange little concept called "heat."*

. . .

Here's the deal with Eric's family. Until we got married, I never had the chance to ask Eric if he had any relatives, because, as we've established, I couldn't talk. And even if I had been able to talk, it would've felt a bit insensitive to ask, "Hey, so I noticed it's just you and this creepy butler all alone in this giant castle. Is your entire family dead? What's the situation here?"

But, yes, Eric does have a family. In fact, his father, older brother, sister-in-law, and grandparents are all very much alive. They just happen to live in an even bigger castle in the Kingdom's capital a few miles inland. That's right, the giant castle Eric lives in isn't even the *real* castle. It's more like their summer cottage, which is wild considering there are people in the Kingdom that are so poor that they sneak into the royal stables at night to steal oats from the horses. Let's just say I can see why some people aren't huge fans of the monarchy.

But I digress. The reason Eric was hanging out solo in the summer castle with Grumpy McWeirdo was so that he could complete his mandatory military service in the royal navy. Which explains why he was on that huge sailboat where his ass almost drowned the day I met him. How the crew failed to spot the giant low-pressure system forming offshore, I'll never know. But I guess it was fate that I happened to be there that day to save him.

Not that his family has ever given me credit for it.

But that's a whole other story.

. . .

I swear to God, Eric is obsessed with boats. His number-one hobby is to drag me to the cliffs overlooking the water and point out all of the boats. "That one over there is a schooner! That one there is a frigate! That little one is a sloop! And the one heading into the harbor is a clipper ship!"

Meanwhile, I'm thinking, *"frigate" is right. Because I would "schooner" die than listen to any more of this stupid boat talk.*

. . .

Fish, crabs, and birds could all talk, but dogs couldn't? Land really had me going like, "Whaaaaaat?"

. . .

Eric's brother, Wilhelm, is married to this chick named Katarina that used to be an elf, and everyone in the kingdom is *obsessed* with her. The newspaper is constantly printing stories about her like "Princess Katarina Dazzles in Mermaid Dress at Royal Ball."

Meanwhile, what are they printing about me? An actual mermaid? Stories like "Prince Eric's Tight-Lipped New Beau: Stuck-Up? Or Just Really Dull?" and "Royal Quack? Deranged Princess Ariel Spotted Outside Castle Talking To Bird." Which is bullshit, by the way, because I see humans talk to dogs all the time even though they can't communicate with each other, which is 1,000 times more unhinged in my opinion.

. . .

One day, Eric bursts into our royal bed chamber, and he goes "Ariel, you *have* to read this book that just came out! It's got everything: action, adventure, tales of faraway lands, the struggles of humanity against nature, a cautionary tale of one man's gradual descent into madness amid his reckless pursuit of an unattainable goal, boats, everything!"

Then he hands me the largest book I have ever seen in my life. Mind you, I'm still trying to get my bearings on this whole "reading" thing at this point. Paper disintegrates pretty quickly in the ocean, so we don't exactly have a lot of literature down there. The only writing we have underwater is in the form of soul-binding contracts forged in magical squid ink by sea witches that are written in intentionally vague legalese with a lot of fine print that most merpeople don't bother to read. That is, if you even know how to read, which most of us don't. That's how they get you.

Point is, I was not excited to struggle my way, word by word, through this tome. But I figured, if Eric thinks I'd like it, then I ought to give it a shot. So I spent the next seven months thumbing my way through page after page of descriptions of what the ocean looks like (I lived in it, I already know what it looks like) and painstaking detail about how every single part of a boat works (why, pray tell, would I ever need to know how to trim a Mizzen topsail?).

But the real kicker is, the *entire* book is about people trying to kill a whale. And, as you can imagine, humans brutally murdering sea creatures is a bit of a sore spot for most merpeople, myself included.

I guess, in retrospect, maybe it was a red flag that Eric fell in love with me without us having a single conversation about our interests. Though, in his defense, I can see how being raised to believe that

God ordained your family to rule over your entire Kingdom might make you a little self-focused.

. . .

Yes, Eric's grandmother actually asked if the baby was going to be born with *flippers*. I'm not making that up. I'm telling you, these people's ignorance truly knows no bounds.

. . .

You know what happens when you "spend all day in the sun?" Your skin feels like someone lit it on fire, which, as I alluded to earlier, hurts like hell. There's this scientist named Charles Darwin who's been traveling around giving talks about how humans and other land animals may have come from fish that decided to crawl out of the sea. Why a fish, millions of years ago, would decide to stay up here on this hot, dry, desolate hellscape—where too much sun can literally kill you—is beyond me.

Yes, I realize how ironic that statement is coming from me. But that fish wasn't an impressionable sixteen-year-old staring into the piercing blue eyes of the first handsome human she'd ever laid eyes on.

. . .

Princess Katarina always orders seafood when the royal family dines together, and I'm beginning to think she's doing it on purpose. Bitch.

. . .

Leaving the royal family wasn't an easy decision. So many people in the Kingdom were outraged, especially after Eric and I did that seaside interview with Orca Winfrey. But we felt like we deserved the opportunity to share our side of the story publicly.

And sure, Orca Winfrey may not be as well known on land, but she is highly respected in Atlantica. And she's no softie. She has a killer instinct, after all. So it's not like she was lobbing softballs at us the entire time. She really grilled us on a lot of things. Especially Eric's role in the fishing industry, which as you can probably imagine, hit close to home for her.

All in all, I felt like it was a very fair interview, although I will admit that some things did get lost in translation. But that's mostly because I had to do all of the translating for Eric and my Whale has gotten a little rusty since going ashore.

. . .

I'm not sure what a normal age for humans to marry each other is. But I was sixteen years old and, looking back, that seems awfully young. Prince Eric is, let's just say, *older*. Old enough that his advisors were like, "When are you *finally* going to settle down, Eric?" So, you know, not young.

At no point was this more apparent than on our wedding night. I've had lady parts for all of three days at this point and I'd been so busy trying to win Eric over, and fight Ursula to free my father's eternal soul, that I'd barely even had time to look at my lady parts, let alone figure out how they worked.

So, after the wedding, he picks me up and carries me off to the berth of the ship (berth is boatspeak for bedroom, which I only know thanks to that stupid book), pulls off his little naval regalia with the frilly shoulder pads (I though a simple suit would have sufficed but I guess it's tradition for royals to look like total asshats on their wedding day), lowers his pants, hops onto the bed, and says, "You know what to do."

Needless to say, dear reader, I did not know what to do.

The thing you need to understand is that merpeople do not reproduce the way humans reproduce. Remember, we're fish from the waist down. So I'm expecting humans to reproduce the same way we do: the female finds a nice cozy spot to lay her eggs, which come out of her papilla. Then, whenever the male feels up for it, he comes by and fertilizes the eggs with sperm, which comes out of his very similar-looking papilla. And then we both go about our lives for a while until the eggs hatch. At which point, I'm assuming our twenty to thirty little human babies will be able to walk and feed themselves and be relatively self-sufficient right out the gate.

So I'm a little surprised when his pants come off and there's a weird sea slug–looking thing in between his legs and he's pointing at it and grinning like I know exactly what I'm supposed to do with that freaky-ass appendage.

But, at that moment, I did remember that I had seen something like that before. Because dolphins, horny fuckers of the ocean that they are, also have those appendages, and I've seen them do all sorts of freaky dolphin shit with them. I'm talking sticking them in other dolphin's blowholes, inside decapitated fish like some sort of sex sleeve, all kinds of fucked up shit. Don't try to look it up because I'm sure if humans have somehow observed dolphin sex and written books about it, those books are definitely banned by the church. Dolphin sex is some fucked up shit.

Now that I've seen his appendage, I'm thinking, *Okay, humans have sex like dolphins, they stick those appendages in all sorts of weird places, and do all sorts of other weird things with them. So let's just try some stuff and see what he likes.* So, I do the first thing that comes to mind, which is something I've seen dolphins do a million times. I cup my hand into the most rigid, fin-like paddle I can, cock my arm back, and give his little sea slug the hardest smack I can muster.

Suffice it to say, he did not enjoy that as much as dolphins seem to.

Our sex life has since gotten better, especially after I discovered, years later and entirely on my own, that my parts (my clam to his slug) are also capable of feeling really, really good. Which, of course, Eric knew nothing about and showed relatively little interest in exploring. Probably because all of the books about how my parts work have also been banned by the church.

. . .

Well, folks, if you thought *my* memoir was intense, wait until you read Prince Eric's memoir, *Spear.* It's raunchy, it's riveting, and it reveals tons of other juicy details about the royal family that my book barely scratched the surface of.

I'm totally kidding. It's 379 pages about boats.

S. Hrg. 117-235

HEARING ON APPROPRIATIONS FOR FISCAL YEAR 2023

REGARDING STRATEGIC DSS AND FBI COUNTERTERRORISM

OPERATIONS CODE NAMED FAST AND FURIOUS

TESTIMONY OF MR. DOMINIC TORETTO

BEFORE THE

COMMITTEE ON THE BUDGET UNITED STATES SENATE

ONE HUNDRED SEVENTEENTH CONGRESS

SECOND SESSION

March 30, 2022

Printed for the use of the Committee on the Budget

U.S. GOVERNMENT PUBLISHING OFFICE

47-314   WASHINGTON : 2022

CONTENTS

WEDNESDAY, MARCH 30, 2022

Page

OPENING STATEMENTS BY COMMITTEE MEMBERS

WITNESS

THE PRESIDENT'S FISCAL YEAR 2023 BUDGET PROPOSAL

WEDNESDAY, MARCH 30, 2022

U.S. SENATE,
COMMITTEE ON THE BUDGET,
Washington, D.C.

The Committee met, pursuant to notice, at 11:00 a.m., via Webex
and in Room SD-608, Dirksen Senate Office Building, Hon. Bernard
Sanders, Chairman of the Committee, presiding.

Present: Senators Sanders, Murray, Stabenow, Whitehouse, War-
ner, Merkley, Kaine, Van Hollen, Lujan, Padilla, Graham, Grassley,
Crapo, Toomey, Johnson, Braun, Scott, Romney, and Kennedy.

Staff Present: Warren Gunnels, Majority Staff Director; and
Nick Myers, Republican Staff Director.

OPENING STATEMENT OF CHAIRMAN SANDERS

Chairman SANDERS: Okay. Let us get to business. Let me thank
everyone for being here this morning, and thank you, Mr. Toretto,
for joining us.

As we begin this hearing, let us be very clear. Budgets reflect
who we are as the American people. They reflect who in society
we value and who we ignore. And I believe that every dollar that
the Federal Government spends should be used to directly benefit
the American working class, not lining the pockets of wealthy
auto company CEOs, and the military-industrial complex.

As we discuss appropriations for the so-called Fast and Furious program, we should be asking ourselves whether this funding
will materially ensure the safety of the people of the United States,
or is this program just another handout to the corporations who

manufacture expensive automobiles, gadgets, and weapons so that people like Mr. Toretto can parade around the globe destroying property, damaging critical infrastructure, and sowing ill will in countries around the world.

We are living at a time when the wealthiest people in our country are becoming phenomenally wealthier, while over half of the people in this country are living paycheck to paycheck. We, as a government, should ensure that taxpayer dollars go to the families that need it most, not to the oligarchs raking in profits by building weaponized luxury convertibles and classic American muscle cars designed to engage in high-speed pursuits on the streets of iconic cities across the globe.

It is up to Congress to act responsibly as we consider appropriations for this needless defense program. As Chairman of the Senate Budget Committee I will be doing everything I can to pass a strong and robust budget spending bill that works for working families, not the 1 percent who profit off of the high-stakes, winner-take-all world of street-racing-centered espionage.

With that let me now recognize the Ranking Member of this Committee, Lindsey Graham.

OPENING STATEMENT OF SENATOR GRAHAM

Senator GRAHAM: Thank you, Mr. Chairman, and here is the other view. The world is on fire, and if you do not believe me, turn on your television. Hackers are trying to get their hands on biometrically activated malware that can infiltrate any computer-controlled system on Earth. Cyberterrorists are attempting to steal military-grade EMP devices that could bring entire countries to their knees. The budget Chairman Sanders has proposed would be woefully inadequate in addressing these threats and, if I'm being honest, is just plain irresponsible.

When you look over the next decade at how much we plan to spend on defense, you have to ask yourself: the threats we face, are they getting smaller or larger? Just look at the plots Mr. Toretto and his team have thwarted over the past two decades. It seems like every two or three years, they stop one deadly threat to this country right in its tracks, and then along comes another, even more deadly, more existential threat to the country. And Mr. Toretto and his colleagues again have to use their expert knowledge of auto mechanics and precision driving skills to bring these cyberterrorists, shadowy crime syndicates, and cybernetically enhanced supervillains to justice. Mr. Toretto is a patriot and an American hero. But Senator Sanders paints him as some vigilante gallivanting around the world in some fancy supercar at the expense of the American people. That could not be further from the truth.

The Chairman said something I agree with. Budgets reflect who we are and what world we live in. Do we want to be the kind of country that sits on the sideline while bad guys try to hijack nuclear submarines in order to start a worldwide nuclear war? Or do we want to be the kind of country that equips its heroes with the 900 horses of Detroit muscle they need in order to keep the American people safe?

I welcome a healthy debate and a vote on this budget as presented, and I hope we can agree that the American people, and the brave men and women who defend them, deserve better than this budget as it stands now. Thank you, Mr. Chairman.

Chairman SANDERS: Thank you, Senator Graham.

Our witness today is Mr. Dominic Toretto. He is, as we have

mentioned, a member of the joint DSS and FBI counterintelligence and counterterrorism operation codenamed Fast and Furious, and we welcome him for being with us today. Thank you very much for being here, Mr. Toretto.

STATEMENT OF MR. DOMINIC TORETTO, LEAD TEAM MEMBER OF SPECIAL OPERATION FAST AND FURIOUS

DOMINIC TORETTO: Thank you...uhh...Chairman Sanders, Ranking Member Graham, members of the Committee, thank you for the opportunity to testify today. And please, Senators, call me Dom.

So...uhh...I'm not really one for speeches, I'm more of an "actions speak louder than words" kinda guy. So I guess I'll start by talking about what me and my team do, what sorta missions we've been on over the past couple years, what the team means to me, and what the team means to America.

My crew and I run covert ops around the world trying to stop bad people from doing bad things. You got your, uh, standard electromagnetic pulses, your superviruses, Project Aries (that computer thing that looked kinda like the Times Square New Year's Eve Ball), and more. We basically go in and stop the threats using each of our skill sets, a combination of sharpshooting, hand-to-hand combat, computer hacking, high-speed racing, and car repair.

My crew are like family to me, and we Torettos believe family is everything. That's why I like to think of America as my family, too. You are all my cousins, including you, senators. And I know family doesn't always get along, but we have to look out for each other. That's what I do for America. Because my family is my family, and my crew is my family, and America is also my family. Thank you.

Senator SANDERS: Thank you, Dom. I, too, like to think of America as a family, and that family should look out for one another. Which is why I support increasing taxes on the billionaires and the 1 percent. Now, let me ask you this. In June of last year, you were involved in a covert operation in Montequinto, a sovereign nation in Central America. Is that correct?

DOMINIC TORETTO: Yeah.

Senator SANDERS: And it didn't go so well, did it?

DOMINIC TORETTO: We ran into some issues.

Senator SANDERS: You certainly did. I have in front of me the headline that ran in the *Huffington Post* the next day: "Secret Spy Plane Crashes in Hostile Country Followed by Covert Ops Firefight." Does that ring a bell?

DOMINIC TORETTO: Yeah, I remember Agent Stasiak mentioning that.

Senator SANDERS: Dom, may I remind you that the United States does not have diplomatic relations with Montequinto and considers them to be a hostile nation?

DOMINIC TORETTO: Yeah, I kinda found that out the hard way.

Senator SANDERS: Precisely. As I recall, you narrowly escaped by latching your car to the remains of a rope bridge on the border of Montequinto and swinging your car from the Montequinto side of the canyon to the Nicaraguan side. Pretty impressive driving.

DOMINIC TORETTO: Thanks.

Senator SANDERS: What's not so impressive is that you totaled your military-issue Dodge Charger SRT Hellcat. Are you familiar with Dodge's contract for building Charger SRT Hellcats for the United States Special Forces?

DOMINIC TORETTO: Can't say that I am.

Senator SANDERS: Well, I am. And do you know how much the United States government pays Stellantis North America, the parent company of Fiat Chrysler, who manufactures the Charger SRT Hellcat?

DOMINIC TORETTO: Nope.

Senator SANDERS: Five point two million dollars. That's quite a bit more than I paid for my 2011 Chevy Aveo. Cars with built-in turbo buttons do not come cheap.

DOMINIC TORETTO: I guess not.

Senator SANDERS: I bring this up, not to disparage your driving skills, Mr. Toretto, but to remind my fellow committee members that these covert operations in sovereign nations are expensive and middle class taxpayers are the ones left footing the bill.

Senator GRAHAM: Dominic. Let me ask you something? Are cartel leaders bad?

DOMINIC TORETTO: Yeah, they're pretty bad.

Senator GRAHAM: Are terrorists bad?

DOMINIC TORETTO: Yeah.

Senator GRAHAM: Are computer hackers bad?

DOMINIC TORETTO: Sure.

Senator GRAHAM: And you and your team, you're in charge of arresting those kinds of people, is that right?

DOMINIC TORETTO: Yeah.

Senator GRAHAM: But the way Chairman Sanders talks about it, it sounds like he doesn't want you stopping those bad people from doing bad things, doesn't it?

DOMINIC TORETTO: I guess so.

Senator GRAHAM: Dom, could you describe Project Aries for me?

DOMINIC TORETTO: Yeah, it's basically a computer that lets you take control of any computer on Earth.

Senator GRAHAM: Even the computers with all the nuclear codes?

DOMINIC TORETTO: Especially the computers with all the nuclear codes.

Senator GRAHAM: So if it were to fall into the wrong hands, that would be pretty bad, wouldn't it?

DOMINIC TORETTO: For sure.

Senator GRAHAM: But you and your team stopped that from happening, correct?

DOMINIC TORETTO: We did.

Senator GRAHAM: If memory serves, you courageously raced through the streets of Tbilisi in a '68 Charger 500 in order to prevent Project Aries from being uplinked to the satellite that would allow it to take over the world's computing systems, isn't that right?

DOMINIC TORETTO: Well, it was a team effort, but yeah, I drove the '68 Charger.

Senator GRAHAM: And would you say the supercharged 6.2-liter V8-powered Hellcat engine—that's assembled in my great home state of South Carolina—was instrumental in helping you chase down the armored trailer where the uplink was taking place?

DOMINIC TORETTO: Nothing beats American muscle.

Senator GRAHAM: I couldn't agree more, Mr. Toretto. It's a shame Senator Sanders doesn't feel the same way.

Senator SANDERS: I am a staunch supporter of the American auto industry, which has created thousands of high-paying manufacturing jobs that provide hardworking Americans with a path to the middle class. But that does not justify building supercharged vehicles to cause millions of dollars of collateral damage racing around the nation of Georgia, which, I will remind Senator Graham, is a strategic ally of the United States.

Senator GRAHAM: Tell that to the good people of the Columbia,

South Carolina metropolitan area who would lose their jobs if the Hellcat plant were shut down.

Mr. Toretto, don't you think a little collateral damage is worth it to create good jobs in a right-to-work state while also saving the world? Seems like a win-win, right? After all, there was no other way to stop the satellite uplink, right?

DOMINIC TORETTO: Well, it turned out we didn't really need to destroy the armored trailer since my boys Tej and Roman blew up the satellite.

Senator GRAHAM: I'm sorry, what's that now?

DOMINIC TORETTO: Yeah, they strapped a rocket to a Pontiac Fiero—don't ask me how, 'cause I know nothing about rockets—and flew it into the satellite. So that kinda took care of everything. I guess, looking back, we could've just done that.

Senator GRAHAM: Well, you wanted to retrieve Project Aries from your brother, right? So that he wouldn't try to uplink it again?

DOMINIC TORETTO: I guess so, but now that I'm thinking about it—we had both halves of Project Aries. We could've just destroyed it. Hell, one half doesn't even work without the other one and both of the inventors are dead, so we could've probably just destroyed the first half the minute we found it in Montequinto. Man, that would've saved us a lot of headaches, 'cause we really did do a lot of damage in Tbilisi. So many totaled cars. Which sucks, 'cause I love cars. I really love cars.

Senator GRAHAM: Huh, okay, well, let me think. Oh! But you still had to go after your brother because he's a rogue agent turned criminal mastermind. So you had to go after him!

DOMINIC TORETTO: Yeah, but to be honest, I was never gonna let my kid brother get locked up. He's family.

Senator GRAHAM: I see.

Senator SANDERS: You bring up an excellent point, Mr. Toretto. Let's talk about the effectiveness of the Fast and Furious program. In the years since you've been cooperating with law enforcement as a member of this special ops team, have you caught every criminal you've been after?

DOMINIC TORETTO: No, not all of them.

Senator SANDERS: Right, by your own admission, you let your brother, who is still wanted by the FBI and Interpol, slip through your fingers, because he's family. I think we can all sympathize with that. But what about the cyberterrorist known by the alias Cypher? She is not family, correct? Has she been caught?

DOMINIC TORETTO: No, and no, but we're getting close.

Senator SANDERS: What about the notorious criminal matriarch, Queenie Shaw, who you were recently spotted in a luxury vehicle with shortly after she stole a diamond and emerald necklace from an auction? Have you apprehended her?

DOMINIC TORETTO: Not yet.

Senator GRAHAM: What about that Otto guy? The spoiled, rich prick? He was a pretty terrible actor. And by actor, I of course mean actor in the political sense. Your team managed to take him out, didn't you?

DOMINIC TORETTO: Yeah, but turns out he actually had diplomatic immunity in Georgia, so killing him created more problems than it solved.

Senator GRAHAM: Huh.

Senator SANDERS: It seems to me like spending billions of dollars to almost catch criminals is not a wise use of federal funding. The property damages alone that this operation has incurred over the last twenty years would be enough to provide free, high-quality, nutritious school lunches for two million American children for an entire year. Those cars you and your team drive may be fun to zip around in. Some might even say they're "cool," or "awesome," or "bitchin'." But you know what's not bitchin', Mr. Toretto? Childhood obesity. Nothing bitchin' about that.

Now, I want to take a moment to talk about the history of this covert program and how it has grown from a local FBI operation into a wasteful boondoggle that does nothing but fill the coffers of the ultrarich.

Let's rewind back to 2001, over twenty years ago if you can believe it, back when I was a congressman with an almost full head of hair, which should really tell you it's been a long time. The Los Angeles field office of the FBI was investigating a string of robberies committed using after-market modified street-racing cars. Allow me to read an excerpt from their mission directive:

"Our plan has three simple steps: 1) Find a cop who's good at driving a car, 2) get him to infiltrate the high-octane world of illegal street racing, and 3) use his intel to bust the criminals behind the spate of armed robberies of long-haul trucks in greater Los Angeles. We are partnering with the LAPD to find an undercover officer with the driving skills necessary for this task force. In the meantime we are asking the FBI director for one '95 Mitsubishi Eclipse to be retrofitted with aftermarket enhancements in order to compete against the toughest and fastest drag racers of the Los Angeles underworld."

Not a bad way to spend $10,000. I believe those were your exact words when you inspected the car, right, Mr. Toretto?

DOMINIC TORETTO: Yeah, I remember that car. Cool air intake, a NOS fogger system, T4 Turbo, AIC controller, direct port nitrous injection...

Senator SANDERS: And a stand-alone fuel management system, correct. Now, as I understand it, that car was driven by a former officer, and your friend and brother-in-law Mr. Brian O'Conner, is that correct?

DOMINIC TORETTO: Yep, good ol' Bullet.

Senator SANDERS: Right. And that vehicle—which was purchased for Agent O'Conner so he could race against you, earn your respect, and become a member of your crew—cost $16,000 in today's dollars. What happened to that vehicle on the day it was raced?

DOMINIC TORETTO: Well, first the engine briefly caught on fire. Then it was shot at. And eventually it blew up.

Senator SANDERS: And all of that happened on the very first night?

DOMINIC TORETTO: Yep.

Senator SANDERS: A pretty bad investment, wouldn't we all agree? And yet the Los Angeles field office of the FBI continued to financially support Agent O'Conner's efforts, only for Agent O'Conner to turn and allow you to evade capture, is that right?

DOMINIC TORETTO: Yeah, my boy Bullet really did me a solid back there. That's why Brian will always be family. I actually named my first-born son Brian.

Senator SANDERS: Yes, we're aware of your affinity for family, Mr. Toretto. My point is, the LAPD and FBI's efforts ultimately proved unsuccessful at deterring illegal street racing, and street-racing-related crimes.

But just two months later, the September 11th attacks occurred, and every regional FBI task force was given blank checks to pursue any terrorist and criminal activities they saw fit. And so the Fast and Furious program endured. Now, two decades later, this regional sting operation has spiraled into an international intelligence program that has wasted billions of dollars in equipment costs, maintenance, fuel, and civil court damages everywhere from Edinburgh to Rio de Janeiro.

DOMINIC TORETTO: Oh man, Rio, now that was a great time.

Senator GRAHAM: Okay. Let's set all that aside for just a minute. So you've destroyed some property in a couple countries around the world? Big deal. The point is, you and your colleagues are carrying out important work thwarting terrorists' efforts to take over the world. Isn't that something we should all be celebrating and supporting? Do we really want to be the country that sees British siblings who are former MI6 and SAS members turned mercenaries wreaking havoc around the world, and doesn't do everything in our power as a nation to stop them? Things that include but are not limited to using high-performance, custom-built cars specifically designed for chasing bad guys?

Sure, sometimes, as part of your work, you completely destroy those vehicles by driving them straight over cliffs, ramming them into tanks, or launching them from one skyscraper to another. And sure, along the way sometimes restaurants, retail outlets, and other small businesses get completely obliterated as you drive your supercars through their shop windows. But every storefront window that gets smashed is a storefront window that gets smashed in the name of freedom. And in the name of delivering economic prosperity to hardworking Americans without needless regulations and labor unions.

DOMINIC TORETTO: Plus, it helped keep me out of prison. I did two years in Lompoc and I swore I'd never go back.

Senator GRAHAM: I'm sorry, what now?

Senator SANDERS: You were incarcerated?

DOMINIC TORETTO: Who do you think was behind that string of armed truck robberies?

Senator GRAHAM: So we have a former criminal running covert operations around the world?

DOMINIC TORETTO: Pretty much our entire team other than Brian was locked up at one point.

Senator SANDERS: Well, I commend you for turning your life around, Mr. Toretto. Prison recidivism is a huge problem in this country. Millions of Americans are incarcerated, most of them Black and Brown, more than any other nation on Earth. That is why I am a staunch opponent of private prisons and the prison industrial complex, and an advocate for programs that give people like yourself second chances in exchange for serving our country.

DOMINIC TORETTO: Thank you. That means a lot. It really does.

Senator SANDERS: Well, this changes everything.

Senator GRAHAM: Yes, this changes everything.

Senator SANDERS: I may have to rethink whether I can support this program.

Senator GRAHAM: I'm also gonna have to rethink whether I can support this program.

Senator SANDERS: Thank you, Mr. Toretto, for being here to share your story.

DOMINIC TORETTO: Sure thing, anything for my extended family, America.

Senator GRAHAM: Motion to table this item of the budget resolution.

Senator SANDERS: All in favor say aye.

Senator SANDERS: The motion passes. The next defense budget line item regards $50 million in appropriations as part of the CIA's strategic partnership with the MI6 covert operation known as 007...

Meanwhile, at a Bar on a Small Tropical Island in the Caribbean...

— So, what do you think of the new guy in town?

— Who, Bund?

— Yeah, Hames Bund. Odd guy, right?

— Seems a little young to be retired.

— According to him, he was in the business of "making a killing" with "high tech."

— Guess that explains the Aston Martin.

— And the 50-foot sailboat.

— And the 3,500-square-foot cliffside villa.

— Kind of jacked for a tech bro, don't you think?

— Apparently he's already slept with half of the wives on the island. Half of the husbands too.

— Did you...

— Yup. You?

— Yup. Gotta say. Bit overconfident? Didn't last very long. Lots of puns.

— SO many puns.

— Also, very picky drinker.

— Right? Ever heard of a daiquiri? Or a mai tai? Patrice makes an unbelievable mai tai.

— This island literally has the most delicious tropical fruits and rums on Earth. And you're knocking back vodka and olives?

— Psychopath behavior.

•　•　•

— Well, don't look now, but guess who just pulled up to the bar in his DB5.

— How did he even get that thing onto the island?

— Guillaume swears he saw Bund drive it up out of the water and onto the beach.

— A submarine car? Gimme a break. Aston Martins are fancy but they're not *that* fancy.

— There goes Bund, ordering the usual. No surprises there.

— As if shaking it is really going to make it taste different. You're still drinking Stoli in the Caribbean. Like an asshole.

— I actually heard the wildest thing the other day.

— What?

— You know Marcel? The cab driver? He told me he thinks Bund used to be a spy.

— Get out of here, man.

— Think about it. The fancy car. The abs. The promiscuity. The telling people, "I used to be a spy" when he gets really drunk.

— You can't trust a damn thing that comes out of Marcel's mouth and you know it. That man listens to too much talk radio.

— I don't know. I think he might be onto something.

— But think about it. If you were a former superspy for a top-secret British intelligence organization and there were hundreds of criminal syndicates, cyber terrorists, and rogue governments that wanted you dead, would you move to a small island, drive the only luxury car around, live in the biggest house, sail around all day on your super fancy sailboat, and be the only white guy around? For miles? Wouldn't you be better off laying low in some mid-sized industrial city like Bristol or Sheffield where nobody's going to give a shit about you or ask too many questions? Instead of a tiny cay where an inquiring mind could show up, ask, "You seen a white guy around here?" and literally everyone would be like, "Oh yeah, big house, end of the road, can't miss it." Wouldn't that be an unbelievably, uncharacteristically stupid thing for someone like that to do?

— I'd probably move to the tropical island, too.

— Yeah, but you're a dumbass.

— Fair.

— Hey, look, a bunch of black SUVs are pulling up. That can't be good.

— We better duck behind the bar.

— Good thought.

· · ·

— Wow, I can't believe he killed fifteen guys with an olive pick.

— I guess you were right.

— Yeah, Jean-Pierre said he saw Bund take off in some sort of stealth plane this morning. Must've had it hidden away somewhere.

— Guess he got dragged out of retirement for one last mission.

— Shame about Patrice, though.

— Best damn bartender on the island.

— Can't believe the last drink he ever made was a fucking vodka martini. That Hames Bund. What an asshole.

— The biggest asshole.

— I will not miss the puns.

— So many goddamn puns.

Our Statement on Diversity, Equity, and Inclusion from the Hogwarts School of Witchcraft and Wizardry

To members of the Hogwarts community,

As the wizarding world emerges from its greatest challenge in history, we were reminded recently that our work is far from over. Just a few short months after the defeat of Lord Voldemort and the end of his wanton pursuit of pure-blood wizarding supremacy, an incident took place involving one of our students that served as a sobering reminder of the challenges we must still overcome as a community. While Voldemort's defeat has ushered in a swift change in attitudes towards wizarding blood purity in recent months, we still have a long way to go when it comes to another closely related evil—racism.

As some of you may know, last weekend, aurors were summoned in response to reports of blood-curdling screams coming from a Hogsmeade residence known as the Shrieking Shack—an abandoned house long known to be a rendezvous point for criminals as well as the site of the tragic slaying of Professor and Hogwarts Headmaster Severus Snape. As I'm writing this, I realize that perhaps an abandoned murder house with a known pathway leading directly to our campus probably should have been torn down a long time ago. But that notwithstanding, what took place in the moments after magical law enforcement were summoned was simply unacceptable.

When aurors arrived at the Shrieking Shack, a Black seventh-year Hogwarts student, Dean Thomas, happened to be walking past on his way back to campus after a visit to Hogsmeade, where he had purchased a bag of Fizzing Whizzbees and a sugar-spun quill from Honeydukes. Thomas was questioned and told to pull out the contents of his bag. When he did this, one of the aurors, mistaking his sugar-spun quill for a wand, placed him under the Cruciatus Curse—a controversial unforgivable curse that aurors are permitted to use only in self-defence and which many activists believe should be banned from auror use-of-magic guidelines altogether.

Needless to say, student safety is our number-one priority at Hogwarts. It may not seem that way given the three-headed dog, the huge snake that spent decades undetected in our plumbing system, the animated willow tree that loves smacking the heck out of people, the forest filled with deadly creatures that we politely ask students not to enter instead of shielding it off with magic, the numerous dangerous potions, plants, and creatures we let the students interact with in class, the lake filled with hostile merpeople, the repeated infiltration of the campus by servants of Lord Voldemort posing either as professors or pets, that one year we let soul-sucking dementors hang out on campus, our choice to arm every student with a weapon capable of causing certain death with two simple words, and the fact that we allowed an epic battle for the fate of the world to take place on our campus.

However, any student being subjected to an unforgivable curse is something we take very seriously. And we have asked the Ministry of Magic to investigate the matter thoroughly, especially given that race may have played a role in why this student was targeted. Rest assured, we will get to the bottom of this and ensure that this never happens again.

That said, in the days following the altercation, Hogwarts students of colour have brought to our attention a number of concerns regarding their treatment on campus. We thank them for their courage in coming forward and we are conducting a comprehensive review of their claims to determine what, if anything, our campus can do better.

Below, I will attempt to address, broadly, the main categories of concern that students brought forward, and what our internal analysis has uncovered thus far regarding each topic:

Campus Diversity

A common complaint that students of colour brought up was the lack of diversity within the Hogwarts community, which has made students of colour feel isolated. We completely understand how lonely it could be to be, for example, the only Chinese student at Hogwarts, or one of just two South Asian students, the other being your identical twin.

In response to these complaints, Hogwarts conducted a head-count of the school's entire student body and staff and found that, of the 280 students enrolled at Hogwarts, only seven identified as students of colour, totalling 2.5 percent of the student body. Of those seven, four students identified as Black, accounting for roughly 1.4 percent of the Hogwarts student body. This percentage indeed lags the demographics of the United Kingdom as a whole as well as other wizarding schools around the world.

Similarly, our audit found only one staff member of colour, Aurora Sinistra, who identifies as Black. Professor Sinistra, who up until this point many students had never heard of, has been instrumental in serving as a bridge between students of colour at

Hogwarts and the administration. It is also important to mention that Professor Sinistra had brought up the lack of diversity at Hogwarts repeatedly at past faculty meetings, and we fully acknowledge that we should have addressed her concerns sooner.

Sadly, after a careful analysis of our options for increasing the diversity of the Hogwarts student body, we have determined that, through no fault of our own, it is not possible for Hogwarts to admit more witches and wizards of colour at this time. This boils down to the Ministry of Magic's strict immigration policies, which puts hard limits on how many witches and wizards of other nationalities can apparate to the United Kingdom and become naturalized citizens. This policy stems from intense lobbying from prominent pureblood wizarding families, who, unsurprisingly, are also intensely xenophobic. So, unfortunately, our hands are tied here.

But it's important to remember that racial identity is just one aspect of diversity, and Hogwarts does very well in other diversity, equity, and inclusion categories. We have continued to steadily grow the number of muggle-born witches and wizards on our campus, as well as the number of animagi, veelas, parseltongues, and metamorphmagi. And when it comes to religious diversity, we are proud to have admitted six Irish Catholic wizards and one witch (all low-income) in the past twelve years, which is a record high!

Curriculum

Students of colour at Hogwarts have also raised concerns that our course curriculum is Eurocentric and fails to prepare students for challenges they may encounter in other parts of the magical world.

Hogwarts does concede that the curriculum does not prepare students for every single potion, spell, or magical creature they may face in other countries. Despite the fact that our Defence

Against the Dark Arts courses do not cover how to protect against regionally specific ghouls and sprites such as chupacabras, wendigo, tokoloshes, or penanggalan, we maintain that it would be impossible to cover every monster, golem, and fiendish apparition on the planet. Which is why we have chosen to stick to a canon of evil beings that students are most likely to encounter while in the UK. If students would like to learn how to defend themselves against ciguapas, or shikigami, or djinn, we believe our course track equips our witches and wizards with the tools to learn that on their own.

Extracurriculars

We have also received multiple requests to broaden the TriWizard Tournament to include all eleven wizarding schools across the globe. Unfortunately, the Ministry already makes it difficult enough for French and Bulgarian students to get visas for the tournament on account of the aforementioned rampant xenophobia. So it's unlikely they'll be amenable to students from Japan or Brazil or Uganda.

It's also worth noting that, the one time we expanded the tournament to four wizards, it was a complete disaster that resulted in the death of a student, so imagine the chaos of a tournament nearly triple the size. Plus, "HendecaWizard Tournament" just doesn't have the same ring to it.

Favouritism

As for the repeated allegations of favouritism among Hogwarts faculty, our records show that just three students (all white) accounted for 94 percent of points awarded to (and deducted from) Gryffindor over the past seven years. So, yes, we fully acknowledge the need to drastically rethink the House Cup points system.

Problematic Legacy

Lastly, there have been calls to rename Slytherin House given that Salazar Slytherin was a prominent owner of house elves. While Hogwarts is committed to the abolition of house elf slavery, we feel that removing the name of one of Hogwarts' founders from the school would erase a significant part of Hogwarts' history. That, and many prominent families whose generous contributions to Hogwarts we rely on for support have said they will no longer donate to the school if Slytherin's name is removed. So this one's a no-go.

Conclusions

We realize that our response may not be satisfying to all students and we regret that there are areas where our administration is simply not in a position to deliver the reforms that witches and wizards of colour have called for. But we must remember that we are a community. And like any community, it is impossible to please every single member of the community at all times. However, we remain committed to working together to make sure all students at Hogwarts feel supported and safe. Or at least relatively safe considering the countless perils present on campus.

Thankfully, our administration has made two major policy changes that we think are crucial steps to healing the racial and ethnic divisions on campus as well as helping witches and wizards of colour feel more supported on Hogwarts' campus.

First, we have created a new staff position: the Faculty Liaison for Equity Matters, or FLEM. This position will be held by Professor Aurora Sinistra and will serve as a way for students to express their needs related to diversity, equity, and inclusion in a safe space. Although initially reluctant, Professor Sinistra has graciously agreed to volunteer her time for this unpaid role, which will involve holding weekly office hours as well as bimonthly student forums. The Hogwarts community extends our most heartfelt thanks to Professor Sinistra for taking on this vital role.

Second, we are pleased to announce that, moving forward, the Defence Against the Dark Arts course track will be renamed Defence Against the Sinister Arts in order to combat the pervasive and problematic stereotype of equating evil with darkness. This is a huge win for more equitable representation on the Hogwarts campus.

I would like to share one final thought with all of you. I know many are still upset by the incident involving beloved Hogwarts student Dean Thomas. But I would urge everyone to remain patient at this time and allow the Ministry of Magic to complete their investigation before we jump to any conclusions about whether race played a role in Mr. Thomas being subjected to the Cruciatus Curse.

Similarly, if charges are brought against the auror who cursed him, we must let the case be heard by Wizengamot and respect due process of wizarding law. Hogwarts must not lose sight of the importance of our institutions, as flawed as they may sometimes be, even as we work to improve the experience of witches and wizards of colour on our campus.

As for the calls for better LGBT+ representation on campus, that's another story. Allowing students to use Polyjuice Potion to change their gender is kind of a non-starter for us.

Sincerely,
Minerva McGonagall
Headmistress, Hogwarts School of
Witchcraft and Wizardry

Life Finds a Way: The Jurassic Park Essays

Sure, the Velociraptors Are Still on the Loose, but That's No Reason Not to Reopen Jurassic Park

Originally published in *McSweeney's Internet Tendency* on May 6, 2020

> *"Trump is shrugging off warnings by scientists that the easing restrictions taking place across the country could cause tens of thousands of deaths."*
> —CNN, 5/6/20

. . .

Hello, Peter Ludlow here, CEO of InGen, the company behind the wildly successful dinosaur-themed amusement park Jurassic Park. As you're all aware, after an unprecedented storm hit the park, we lost power and the velociraptors escaped their enclosure and killed hundreds of park visitors, prompting a two-month shutdown of the park. Well, I'm pleased to announce that, even though the velociraptors are still on the loose, we will be opening Jurassic Park back up to the public!

Now, I understand why some people might be skeptical about reopening an amusement park when there are still blindingly fast, 180-pound predators roaming around. But the fact of the matter is, velociraptors are intelligent, shifty creatures that are not going to be contained anytime soon, so we might as well just start getting used to them killing a few people every now and then. Some might argue

that we should follow the example of other parks that have successfully dealt with velociraptor escapes. But here at Jurassic Park, we've
never been ones to listen to the recommendations of scientists, or
safety experts, or bioethicists, so why would we start now?

As some of you know, Dr. Ian Malcolm, our lead safety consul-
tant, had recommended that we wait until the velociraptors have
been located and contained before reopening the park, so he wasn't
thrilled when we told him the news. I believe his exact words were,
"You were so preoccupied with whether you could reopen the park,
you didn't stop to think whether you should." Talk about a guy on a
high horse.

That said, you'll be pleased to know that, rather than double
down on our containment efforts, we've decided to dissolve the velociraptor containment task force altogether, and focus instead on
how we can get people back into the park as quickly as possible. So
rather than concentrating on so-called life-saving measures like
"staying in designated safe areas" or "masking your scent," we'll be
focusing on the details that will get our customers really excited,
like a wider selection of fun hats, a pterodactyl-shaped gondola ride
to the top of the island, and a brand-new Gordon Ramsay–designed
menu at the Cretaceous Cafe.

In addition to satisfying our customers, the decision to reopen
the park is also about allowing the furloughed employees of Jurassic
Park to get back to the work they love. Could we have continued to
pay their salaries for several months until we got the velociraptor
situation under control? Definitely. We're the wealthiest nature preserve on the planet after all. And will some of the employees returning to work have their limbs torn off and tossed into the air like a
juggler tossing bowling pins? Undoubtedly. But we're confident that
with a few safety precautions put in place, we'll be able to keep the

level of workplace injuries and deaths just below levels that would elicit widespread public outrage. And keeping things just below widespread public outrage levels is our gold standard for all of the decisions we make here at Jurassic Park.

And speaking of injuries, I want to take a moment to thank our Jurassic Park EMTs. They're the real heroes here, am I right? In the process of responding to velociraptor attacks, many of our EMTs get mauled and dismembered by velociraptors themselves. That's why, as a sign of appreciation, we will be repainting the Jurassic Park ambulance with the words "Hero Mobile" in big bubble letters. We think this is a far more meaningful token of gratitude than the salary increase they requested.

I know many of you out there are going to be hesitant to return to Jurassic Park knowing there are still velociraptors roaming the preserve, but rest assured things will return to normal sooner rather than later. The life expectancy of a velociraptor is only fifteen to twenty years, so we're confident that these attacks will eventually run their course.

In the meantime, will more visitors die? Yes. Will more Jurassic Park staff die? Yes. But know that their sacrifice will not be forgotten—we plan to erect a small plaque dedicated to all of the velociraptor attack victims in the far back corner of the gift shop next to the T-shirts that say I SURVIVED A VISIT TO JURASSIC PARK AND ALL I GOT WAS THIS LOUSY T-SHIRT. It's the least we could do.

So pack your suitcases, and get ready to be reacquainted with the newly reopened, and only slightly more dangerous, Jurassic Park! And remember, life finds a way...unless you're one of the unlucky ones that gets attacked by a velociraptor, then you're probably screwed.

We Shouldn't Presume That the Velociraptor Experts Know the Best Way to Deal With Velociraptor Attacks

Originally published in *McSweeney's Internet Tendency* on July 1, 2020

> *"Sen. Rand Paul aggressively questioned the guidance of federal health experts at a Senate committee hearing Tuesday, including Dr. Anthony Fauci, arguing that Americans 'just need more optimism,' despite the fact there are currently more than 2.6 million confirmed cases of COVID-19 in the U.S., resulting in more than 125,000 deaths... 'We shouldn't presume that a group of experts somehow knows what's best for everyone,' said Paul."*
> —*Forbes*, 6/30/20

. . .

Hello, Peter Ludlow here again with an update from the recently reopened Jurassic Park. First, let me just say that we are completely blown away by how willing and eager people have been to revisit Jurassic Park. The Cretaceous Cafe is packed with tourists, and our three hundred miles of trails are full of hikers eager to experience the magic our wonderful dinosaur amusement park has to offer. Believe me when I say that your loyalty and continued patronage mean the world to us.

Now, I know there have been reports that Jurassic Park is now in the midst of a second wave of velociraptor attacks even deadlier than the first wave. And that the second wave is mostly due to the fact that, during the closure of the park, we spent all of our resources on building new amenities and not on improving park safety. However, I can assure you that the increase in attacks is simply due to our vigilant park rangers who patrol the hiking trails each morning and count the number of human bones they find on the sides of each trail. With more rangers patrolling the grounds these days, of course we are going to find more human remains, which is why I've repeatedly said that the morning patrols are a double-edged sword. And to those who say that those types of statements make it sound like I view the velociraptor attacks as more of a PR crisis than a public safety crisis, let me make one thing clear: I absolutely view this as a PR crisis.

Don't get me wrong; I was just as devastated as anyone else when I heard the news that a group of children whose parents had let them hike the Raptor Ridge trail unattended were subsequently mauled by velociraptors, their desiccated remains strewn about the path like a Jackson Pollock painting made of human flesh. But keep in mind that for every child that's torn apart by velociraptors, there are at least five or six that manage to thwart the attacks by hiding in industrial kitchens and throwing pots and pans at just the right moment to distract the velociraptors and narrowly escape. And with those kinds of odds, do we really need to impinge on the freedom of parents to do what they feel is best for their children?

As for the experts like Dr. Ian Malcolm, who claim that we could drastically reduce the number of velociraptor attacks simply by requiring hikers to mask their scents and closing the crowded trails where the velociraptors have been known to attack? I think it's important that we not simply take their advice for granted, but also consider the opinions of people who haven't dedicated their entire lives to studying ways to prevent these types of attacks. I, for one, don't mask my scent when I go for hikes in the park because I was raised to believe that men should always smell like whiskey, sweat, and Paco Rabanne. And I don't see why my views should be any less valid than those of a guy who says things like, "Not masking your scent is the worst idea in the long, sad history of bad ideas." What a Debbie downer!

Instead of "facts" and "data," what our park visitors really need is a healthy dose of optimism. That's why, rather than heeding the pleas of the scientists, we are instead embarking on a marketing campaign to make the velociraptors seem more fun and down to earth. So if someone you know is attacked while visiting Jurassic Park, just remember that Sergeant Pepper, Princess Boopersnoot, and Molly Ringwald are growing boys and girls who need their snacks, and it's not their fault your uncle couldn't run that fast because of his bad hip. Also, don't forget that velociraptor plush toys are now buy one, get two free at the Jurassic Park gift shop, so you can take home all three of our beloved Jurassic Park raptor friends when you visit! Please note that the plush toys have been relocated from their original location at the back of the store since the plaque we erected for the velociraptor attack victims has now been expanded to cover the entire back wall.

That said, there has never been a better time to come visit us at Jurassic Park. Be sure to bring along your friends and family! And as always, remember, life finds a way...unless you're the slowest member of your hiking group. Then you're probably screwed.

Jurassic Park Is Last, Which Means We're First

Originally published in *McSweeney's Internet Tendency* on August 4, 2020

> *"In a contentious interview that aired Monday on 'Axios on HBO,' journalist Jonathan Swan attempted to press President Trump on his handling of the coronavirus pandemic...Trump responded to the climbing death toll by saying 'it is what it is,' and claimed the pandemic is 'under control, as much as you can control it."* —Boston Globe, 8/4/20

. . .

Hello, Peter Ludlow here with yet another update from everyone's favorite dinosaur-themed amusement park, Jurassic Park. There's been a lot of negative press recently about the fact that velociraptor attacks are still happening six months after Sergeant Pepper, Princess Boopersnoot, and Molly Ringwald escaped their enclosure and went on a months-long rampage of death and destruction. And the recent Q2 report showing Jurassic Park's revenue down 32 percent from this time last year is certainly indicative of the disruption these attacks have caused. So I'd like to take a moment to clear the air and reassure our park patrons and investors that everything is under control. The attacks may get worse before they get better, but that's why it's important that I, as park CEO, remind you of the ever-inspiring mantra: It is what it is.

Look, there are some things in life you just can't control. The sun comes up, the sun goes down, the tide comes in, the tide goes out, a pack of velociraptors tears you apart and plays hacky sack with your skull. These are just inevitable parts of life (some might argue that velociraptor attacks are avoidable, but the truth is it's too expensive to justify those prevention measures, so from our perspective, it might as well be inevitable). In any case, that's why it's so important to harness the power of positive thinking. It's the only way we're going to get through this difficult time together. Again, except for those of you that get killed by velociraptors, but don't worry because we've now converted the entire stock room of the gift shop into a memorial to the velociraptor attack victims, so there will be plenty of room for your name on one of the many plaques should the unthinkable happen.

That said, let's focus on the bright side. Like the fact that most velociraptor attack victims survive with just a few missing fingers or toes. And even among those that are severely mauled, the vast majority still pull through. In fact, you'll be pleased to know that Jurassic Park has the highest velociraptor attack survival rate out of any park in the world. Sure, maybe it's because our Jurassic Park EMTs have spent the last six months triaging scores of victims to the point where reattaching dismembered appendages is mere muscle memory for them. But still, how is nobody talking about that!

And that's not the only metric in which Jurassic Park excels. We also lead dinosaur-themed amusement parks in the lowest number of lost limbs per attack (1.3), fastest average limb reattachment time (42 minutes), and fewest people named Ernesto mauled (0, because as a matter of policy, we ban people named Ernesto from entering the park). These are far more meaningful statistics than the "percentage of park patrons attacked" that the media keeps harping on

(62 percent). But if you still don't believe our excellent statistics, just take a look at these charts!

Data

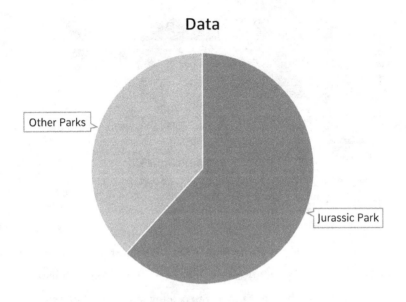

See? Suck on that, other parks!

More Data

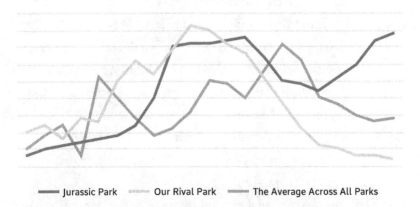

Look at how much progress we are making! Are you kidding me?

Even More Data

Jurassic Park is last, which means we're first!

Given these great stats, I think it should be pretty clear to everyone that reopening the Jurassic Park Academy for Young Paleontologists this fall is the right move. Sure, a few kids have been mauled this summer at our popular sleepaway camp, Camp Triceratops. However, a hands-on learning environment that comes with hiking throughout our vast preserve remains an invaluable experience for the kids—an experience that far outweighs the occasional mauling. Plus, keep in mind that children are far less likely to be killed by velociraptors, mostly because they are too small and bony to make for a satisfying velociraptor meal. And yes, children are notoriously smelly and therefore really good at attracting velociraptors, thus endangering their teachers. But I think it's safe to say the teachers knew the risks involved when they became teachers at a dinosaur-themed amusement park (our old motto "we 100 percent guarantee your safety" notwithstanding).

So let's not get carried away and resort to drastic measures like shutting down the park again, or limiting our beloved educational programs to virtual classes. I am confident that with the modest measures we are taking, the velociraptors will eventually tucker themselves out, and we'll be back to normal sooner rather than later.

Like I always say, life finds a way...unless you're one of the plumper, juicier children in your paleontology class. Then you're probably screwed.

Just Because I Was Mauled by Velociraptors Doesn't Mean I Haven't Done an Excellent Job Handling the Velociraptor Attacks

Originally published in *McSweeney's Internet Tendency* on October 5, 2020

> *"President Donald Trump has had a fever since Friday morning after testing positive for coronavirus, according to a person familiar with the matter, a stunning development that threw a country already unnerved by a devastating health catastrophe and a turbulent political season into fresh upheaval on Friday."* —CNN, 10/2/20

. . .

Hello, Peter Ludlow here, coming to you from the Isla Nublar Medical Center here at Jurassic Park. As you might've heard, on Friday I was mauled by velociraptors while hiking the Raptor Ridge trail along with several other InGen executives. The fact that even our C-suite has been victimized by these sneaky dinosaurs just goes to show how totally unavoidable these attacks are, and why any preventative measures are ultimately futile. And while some have pointed out that no one in our hiking party was masking their scent, and that our CTO had a full beef Wellington tucked away in his backpack, I maintain that enjoying a nice hike while supporting park businesses like the Cretaceous Cafe is well worth the added risk that a sumptuous but also velociraptor-enticing meal poses.

As for the thousands of you who took to social media over the weekend to express your unbridled joy at my misfortune, I simply say: shame on you. Yes, under my leadership, hundreds of park visitors have been viciously mauled by velociraptors, their bony carcasses stripped of flesh, and thrown into a giant pile like crabs at a seafood boil. But that is still not an excuse to poke fun at a man whose actions have literally come back to bite him. That's why we are actively blocking any users who post negative comments about my predicament on Jurassic Park social media pages. And to those that say it's hypocritical to ban these people when we were actively retweeting death threats aimed at Dr. Ian Malcolm less than a week ago, I think I speak for most people when I say that anyone who says things like, "Yeah, but if the Pirates of the Caribbean breaks down, the pirates don't eat the tourists" is clearly asking to be cyberbullied.

On a brighter note, it was so heartwarming to see that group of park patrons gathered outside the Isla Nublar Medical Center to wish me a speedy recovery. In fact, I was so moved by their show of support that I, along with a few park rangers, took them on a hike on Sunday through some of my favorite trails here at the preserve. Some critics are claiming that leaving the hospital to go on a hike when I still had bloody bandages on—which could have potentially attracted velociraptors—was yet another reckless show of disregard for the lives of my park rangers and park patrons. But anyone who knows me knows that I am not one to stay locked up all day hiding from things that are "risky," whether it's going on a dangerous hike, or embarking on a multi-billion-dollar bioethics boondoggle that the *Washington Post* once called "an affront to God."

But speaking of bandages, I want to give a huge shout-out to the amazing Jurassic Park EMTs who bravely came to our rescue in our hour of need, triaging our wounds with a slew of cutting-edge splints and surgical sutures that aren't available to the general public yet. That said, while we still can't accommodate the salary increase you requested due to our tight budget this year (those pterodactyl-shaped gondola cars were all custom-built and they were not cheap), we are pleased to announce that we will be holding an ice cream social for all of our park EMTs this Thursday at 7 a.m.

Lastly, to all of our wonderful InGen shareholders, a heartfelt thank you for continuing to invest in our bold vision for the future of dinosaur-themed entertainment. You may have heard that the board of directors is reportedly considering replacing me next month, and I am calling on you to reach out to them and remind them of all of the great work I've done and why I should stay on as CEO. Sure, we may have more velociraptor-related deaths than any park on Earth, along with staggeringly low park attendance and horrendous staff morale. And, to some, the fact that I was mauled myself might make me look like a senseless moron with a callous disregard for science. However, as bad as things seem now, I can assure you that a new CEO would only make them much worse. So a vote for me is a vote for keeping things as bad as they are now, but probably not any worse. That's a vision I think we can all agree on.

And remember, life finds a way, unless the board of directors replaces me in November. Then you're probably screwed.

Sure, Velociraptor Repellent Is 95 Percent Effective Against Velociraptor Attacks, But Do We Really Need to Wear It to Visit Jurassic Park?

Originally published in *McSweeney's Internet Tendency* on May 4, 2021

> "More than half of adults in the United States have been inoculated with at least one dose of a vaccine. But daily vaccination rates are slipping, and there is widespread consensus among scientists and public health experts that the herd immunity threshold is not attainable...polls show that about 30 percent of the U.S. population is still reluctant to be vaccinated."
>
> —New York Times, 5/3/21

. . .

It's been almost a year since Jurassic Park announced they would be reopening the preserve even though the velociraptors had escaped their enclosure and were still on the loose. Needless to say, it's been a dark chapter in the park's history, as countless Jurassic Park patrons have been mauled, their dismembered body parts and bloody entrails flung haphazardly like fleshy red tinsel on bushes and shrubs throughout the park.

Thankfully, there's some good news: a team of scientists at Jurassic Park's Velociraptor Avoidance and Containment Countermeasures Squadron, or VACCS, have developed a state-of-the-art

velociraptor repellent that is 95 percent effective at preventing velociraptor attacks.

With just two spritzes, one under each armpit, the repellent re-
leases a scent that is completely odorless to humans but, to a velociraptor, smells like an infected velociraptor anal gland, which, needless
to say, is a smell they absolutely hate. Many are calling this new technology an olfactory marvel and have said it's the last piece of the puz-
zle to finally stopping these horrendous velociraptor maulings, which
up until now have been completely unpreventable (aside from taking
a few basic precautions, like not hiking in velociraptor-infested areas,
that were deemed too draconian to actually enforce).

That said, there are many of us long-time Jurassic Park customers who question the need for this so-called miracle spray that the
new park leadership seems so eager to shove up our pits.

As you may recall, former InGen CEO Peter Ludlow was uncere-
moniously ousted recently after a protracted series of corporate legal
battles, mudslinging (a literal mud fight broke out over by the gondola
ride one time), and even a failed boardroom coup. Since then, the new
park leadership has taken drastic steps to try to prevent velociraptor
attacks, including handing out vouchers to encourage patrons to
postpone their visit until it's safe, providing clearer guidelines for
how to responsibly hike the park's trails, and finally listening to the
advice of safety experts like Dr. Ian Malcolm.

Now, with this new repellent available, leadership is encouraging
all park patrons to spray themselves so that the park can achieve
herd immunity—the point at which the herd of velociraptors stops
associating humans with food and moves on to other prey.

But those of us still loyal to Peter Ludlow, or "Luddites" as we
prefer to be called, will not be strong-armed into putting anything
on our bodies that we can't be 100 percent sure wasn't concocted by

a shadowy cabal of elites with ulterior motives like "public safety" and "fewer people being disemboweled by velociraptors."

With this breakthrough technology, could we stop velociraptor attacks once and for all? Sure. But at what cost? Is it really worth saving hundreds of lives if it means park patrons no longer have the freedom to let their odors drift *au natural* and straight into the nostrils of hungry bioengineered dinosaurs the way God intended?

Listen, I get that many people find it infuriating that a large number of Jurassic Park patrons like myself are refusing to don this miraculous and stupidly simple means of preventing mass death while other parks are literally begging VACCS to share their technology with them. But why do you care so much whether I wear repellent or not? If I choose not to wear repellent, and the group of hikers behind me gets viciously torn apart by velociraptors, isn't that on them for being in the wrong place at the wrong time?

Besides, it's so hard knowing who to trust these days. Do I trust Dr. Ian Malcolm, a guy who says smug things like, "Genetic power is the most awesome force the planet's ever seen, but you wield it like a kid that's found his dad's gun"? Or do I trust my friend Gary, an amateur homeopathic healer and die-hard Luddite, who believes the best way to ward off velociraptors is with a balm he makes from patchouli and lawn clippings that he sells out of the back of his Jeep Wrangler for $600 just outside the entrance to the park? It's impossible to say.

So let's all just agree that I'll do me, you do you. And if that means the velociraptors eventually get used to the repellent and we all have to go right back to square one, then so be it.

Just remember, life finds a way...unless you're one of the unlucky 5 percent that wears repellent and still gets mauled. Then you're probably screwed.

A Jurassic Park Post-Mortem

Hello, Peter Ludlow here, coming to you from my private estate on the mainland. It's been over two years since the velociraptors in Jurassic Park got loose and started mauling visitors, prompting a brief shutdown of the park followed by a year and a half of velociraptor containment measures. But, two years, a couple thousand maulings, and one class-action personal injury lawsuit later, I am pleased to announce that the velociraptor outbreak is officially over!

That's right. You are now free to roam about all areas of the park, masking your scent is entirely optional, and you are not required to spray yourself with velociraptor repellent in order to visit the park. Most importantly, the weekly park safety briefings with Dr. Ian Malcolm have been discontinued, which means no more listening to him say snarky things like, "Boy, do I hate being right all the time." That is by far the best part about the restrictions being lifted, if you ask me.

Jurassic Park officially moving on from its attempts to prevent velociraptor attacks speaks to my brilliant leadership back when I was CEO of the park's parent company, InGen. You might remember that I was unfairly ousted from my position as CEO after a shareholder vote that was totally rigged, and after a brave attempt by some of my most loyal shareholders to reinstate me, which, unfortunately, failed. The fact that InGen's legal team is still on my butt about all the bioengineering patents and trade secrets that I supposedly stole as leverage is proof that my ousting wasn't about my performance, but was purely about boardroom politics.

Of course, it's important to mention that, when I say the velociraptor outbreak is "over," I don't mean that velociraptor attacks have stopped happening. Quite the contrary. Velociraptor attacks are still fairly common in the park and visitors continue to get mauled on a daily basis, their bloody guts and organs spilling out of their abdomens as they get ripped apart like a dinosaur piñata.

It's just that now, finally, the media have stopped hyper-fixating on each and every attack, park visitors have grown accustomed to the totally acceptable risk that they might be torn limb from limb at any given moment, and levels of public outrage have finally simmered down to quiet grumbling. Which, as I've said before, has always been the gold standard for decisions made at Jurassic Park.

That said, I want to take this moment to reminisce about my tenure as CEO, reflect on my superior management skills, and discuss all of the ways the new leadership is failing park patrons.

So, what lessons can we learn after dealing with these pesky dinosaurs over the past two-plus years?

First, I think it's safe to say that both the two-month shutdown of the park and the subsequent velociraptor containment measures were a waste of time. Dr. Ian Malcolm insisted on shutting down the park and closing the gates to the Raptor Ridge trail as soon as the first velociraptor maulings took place. But did the two-month shutdown stop the attacks from happening? No, it did not.

The same thing happened when Dr. Malcolm required park visitors to mask their scent and wear repellent when hiking on trails prone to attacks. Despite these measures, the attacks continued. There were even cases of hikers wearing repellant and masking their scent who still got mauled, their corpses shredded into bite-sized chunks along the trail like a human charcuterie board. So it's pretty clear Dr. Malcolm got it wrong every step of the way, which isn't surprising from a guy who glibly says stuff like, "I'll tell you the problem with the scientific power that you're using here. It didn't require any discipline to attain it." What a jackass.

Yes, it's true that the shutdown of the park was never a complete closure. We still allowed limited private tours of the park and there were also plenty of tour companies giving unsanctioned tours who we chose not to crack down too hard on given the financial strain they were under. And yes, we never reached full compliance on masking scent and wearing repellent. But that just proves that park shutdowns and draconian safety measures simply don't work, and that we should've trusted patrons to make the best decisions for themselves and their families. That's what I advocated for from the beginning, and I stand by that to this day.

Another key takeaway is that I was right to focus our efforts on building cool new amenities rather than wasting money on containment efforts. Visitors were going to get mauled no matter what, and, as tragic as it was to learn of their deaths, it was inevitable considering some people just aren't fast enough to outrun velociraptors because they are either elderly or muscularly compromised. Sometimes God's plan for you involves getting decapitated by a seventy-five-million-year-old dinosaur brought back from extinction by extracting its DNA from mosquitoes trapped in amber. And who are we to question the mysterious ways in which God works?

That said, while the park's accounting team repeatedly warned me that the subsequent drop in attendance would vastly outweigh the cost of prevention measures, I still maintain that their numbers were wrong. And if you want proof, just look at how much more expensive it is to visit Jurassic Park now that the new leadership is in charge. Clearly I was doing something right.

There are still plenty of critics out there who will argue that my lax approach to velociraptor containment is why Jurassic Park has had more maulings and lost more revenue than any other dinosaur-themed amusement park. They'll point out that no other park on Earth has had to build an entire new building with floor-to-ceiling plaques just to commemorate all of the visitors and park staff who have lost their lives. They'll point to the hundreds of former Jurassic Park EMTs who left their profession because they were sick of reattaching dozens of severed limbs a day. They'll point to the record levels of distrust that our patrons have of science, some of whom have died after ingesting tonics they were told would ward off velociraptors but were actually just cleaning fluids mixed with paint. And, finally, they'll point out that the park's current financial woes are actually the result of my incompetence and that the new park management is scrambling to clean up the mess I left behind.

To that I say, trust your gut. Would you rather believe a bunch of stuck-up, over-educated elites telling you what you can and can't do? Elites who tell everyone to be fearful of visiting Jurassic Park on account of a couple dinosaurs occasionally chewing people up into human tartare? Or would you rather believe me, the person saying that you can do whatever you want in the park? What is leadership if not letting people go in whatever direction they want to go?

That's why my advice for how to move forward from these past few tragic years is this: dinosaurs kill people, there's nothing we can do about it, and anyone who says otherwise just wants an excuse to boss you around. Once enough people realize that, I'll be more than happy to take back the reins at Jurassic Park and run it like the laissez-faire, free-roaming dinosaur paradise it should be.

In fact, just the other day I heard that a T-Rex got loose at a park in Europe and started eating people. And honestly, if that happened here, I wouldn't even sweat it.

Because remember, life finds a way. Unless there's another deadly dinosaur outbreak in the near future, then you're probably screwed.

What the Fuck Happened to Our House?

Son, I'm trying my best not to lose my temper here, but it's tough when there's a hole the size of a Ford Taurus in our roof and no logical explanation for how it got there.

So I'll ask you one more time, and don't give me any more of that witch crap. What the fuck happened to our house?

As far as your mother and I are concerned, last night was a perfectly normal Halloween night in Salem. The weather was chilly, but calm. There were no tornadoes, or blizzards, or even a drop of rain. So imagine our surprise when, after spending the night dancing at that wicked good party at City Hall, we walk back home in the morning only to look up at our humble abode and see a big-ass gap where the crow's nest used to be.

Admittedly, it was irresponsible to leave you kids unattended all night. But, in our defense, after those three ladies sang that bangin' rendition of Screamin' Jay Hawkins's "I Put a Spell on You," the party really kicked into high gear and we couldn't tear ourselves away no matter how hard we tried. Besides, can you really blame us for wanting to have a night out to ourselves for once?

One tiny parental dereliction of duty is no excuse for whatever behavior led to blowing out the entire top third of the house. Have you been experimenting with improvised explosives in your bedroom? Should we be calling ATF? Max, we didn't move you from LA to Salem for you to become one of those weird kids that looks up how to make pipe bombs "for fun."

What's maybe even more bewildering than the possibility that our son might be the next Unabomber is that you seem to have a complete lack of remorse for the destruction you've caused. We came home to you and your sister giving us huge hugs, with big smiles on your faces like you were living in some kind of happily-ever-after fantasyland. Meanwhile, I have to find a contractor to put a tarp over the roof before a Nor'easter comes through and drops three inches of rain onto the entire goddamn second floor. Which if you knew anything about finding a contractor in Massachusetts, you'd know is going to be a gigantic and stupidly expensive pain in the ass.

And that's just the tip of the iceberg. Because guess what? We can't just do a standard roof repair. Nope. See, you might not be aware of this, but this house is a Second Empire Victorian built in 1870 and is therefore part of the Salem Preservation Society. Which means every repair has to be true to the original appearance of the house, and done exclusively with building materials that were available at the time. That means no vinyl, no laminates, nothing modern. Just hardwood and good old-fashioned slate shingles, which, again, is gonna cost a fucking fortune. Because, Massachusetts.

So you can see why maybe, just maybe, your mother and I are a little miffed when I ask you what the hell happened here, and you give me some cockamamie story about how those three women from the party were actually the infamous Sanderson Sisters, and how they were resurrected because you, a virgin, lit a candle in the old Sanderson Cottage Museum. Although, breaking and entering aside, we are a little relieved to hear that you aren't sexually active yet.

Still, it's beyond insulting to suggest that those nice ladies (who are part of what I can only assume is some sort of immersive theater company, or improv troupe, or cosplay meetup group) were, in fact, unholy servants of Satan on a quest for eternal life. I'm supposed to believe a couple of local thespians were the ones who put a gaping crater in our Italianate-style cupola? Give me a break, Max.

Look, we get it. You're a teenage boy. Teenage boys love to lash out at their parents. They love to be cold and distant. And they love to tell made up stories about evil wiccans, cats with oddly selective talking abilities, and zombies with moths coming out of their mouths. But we're talking about tens of thousands of dollars' worth of home repairs here. Repairs that, if we want them to be covered by our homeowners insurance, are going to require an explanation to the claims adjuster that holds a little more water than "three seventeenth-century sorceresses—with magical powers, bad memories, and a surprisingly deep knowledge of modern pop culture—blasted a hole in our house whilst doin' some witchy shit." Our insurance covers Acts of God. Acts of the Devil, not so much.

So please, for the love of all that is holy, just tell us what actually happened so we can get this house fixed and get our lives back to normal.

And wipe that stupid grin off your face. You and your sister look like you just saved the lives of everyone in Salem instead of looking like two children who are about to be grounded for the rest of the goddamn school year. Also, we have no idea where you got that hideous grimoire with the giant eyeball on it, but it is going straight to Goodwill as soon as they open.

I will say, Allison does seem very nice. Maybe you'll finally lose your virginity!

Beloved Reality Television Star Dead at Age Thirty

LOS ANGELES, CA — This afternoon, the world mourned the loss of beloved reality television star Truman Burbank, whose eponymous program, *The Truman Show*, was the most watched television series of all time and ran for a record thirty straight seasons.

The dramatic series finale of *The Truman Show* saw Burbank sail to the edge of Seahaven Island, the elaborate town-sized set built for the sole purpose of broadcasting Burbank's daily whereabouts. After reaching the edge of the set, Burbank walked to a nearby exit, bid his audience a farewell with his famous catchphrase "In case I don't see you...good afternoon, good evening, and good night," gave a bow, and left the set, ushering in the end of one of the most innovative and controversial television shows in history.

Tragically, Burbank's catchphrase would soon prove true, as, moments after leaving the Paramount Studio lot, Burbank was struck by a city bus traveling westbound on Melrose Avenue.

Eyewitnesses described seeing Burbank walk straight onto the busy thoroughfare, evidently unaware that traffic flow wouldn't immediately halt the moment he crossed the street.

"He just walked right out in front of me. I barely had time to hit the brakes," said bus driver Serge Varlasco, visibly shaken. "I can't believe I [redacted] killed Truman," he later added, fighting back tears.

The show's reclusive creator, known simply by the moniker Christof, issued a brief statement shortly after the actor's death was announced:

> *The entire Truman Show community is shocked and devastated by the loss of our dear friend, Truman Burbank. The entire world watched Truman grow up. From losing his first tooth, to falling in love, Truman endeared himself to all of us and proved to be one of the most compassionate and caring humans to walk this Earth. He will be dearly, dearly missed. Also, Paramount and the Omnicam Corporation take no responsibility for the unfortunate accident caused by Truman's lack of awareness of Los Angeles traffic patterns.*

Burbank's death is yet another in a long line of controversies surrounding *The Truman Show*. The program has repeatedly been accused by human rights watchdogs and ethics groups of violating Truman's right to privacy and intentionally subjecting him to repeated psychological trauma, all while raking in billions of dollars in profits thanks to gratuitous product placement within the show. The "Free Truman" campaign had long called for Truman—the first person to ever be adopted by a corporation—to be released from the show, or to at least be made aware of the show's existence. These calls only grew louder as Truman himself became increasingly aware of his unique life circumstances, leading to a rocky final season which saw Truman spiral into bouts of paranoia—paranoia that ultimately led to Truman holding his wife, Meryl, at knifepoint, resulting in her unexpected departure from the show. Protestors had been gathering outside the Seahaven Island set for weeks leading up to the show's epic finale.

While many fans of *The Truman Show* blamed Christof for Burbank's death, others blamed L.A.'s notoriously car-friendly infrastructure.

"Los Angeles averages twice the pedestrian fatalities per capita of other U.S. cities. This tragedy could have been prevented if the city had invested in dedicated busways and elevated pedestrian crossings as I have repeatedly called for. Amsterdam has installed these all over their city, and vehicle-pedestrian collisions are ten times less frequent than they are here," said a local transit activist and founder of Build Better Busways. Both the spokesperson for LACMTA and the Los Angeles Mayor's Office declined our request for comment on this story, saying the incident was "under review."

Mourners from across the country gathered outside the Paramount lot in the afternoon to leave flowers, teddy bears, and candles. And the two westbound lanes of Melrose Avenue were blocked off to allow fans a chance to gather and celebrate the life of reality television's most famous star. Fans also took to the World Wide Web to express their grief, flooding online chat rooms and message boards with outpourings of sadness. The recently launched communication platform AOL Instant Messenger also reported its largest web traffic to date.

ILuvTruman143: I can't believe Truman is gone! *The Truman Show* was my entire reason for living. What am I supposed to watch now? *Friends?*

Wasaaaaaap78: You will be dearly missed, Truman! Hope you and God are hitting golf balls and pounding Penn Pavel's together in that big Seahaven Island in the sky. RIP.

Emoticonnie36: I am so devastated! I wish keyboards could type little pictographs like cartoon faces or tear drops so I could properly express how sad I am about Truman's death, but sadly nothing like that exists! :'-(

Truman Burbank will be remembered most fondly for his pleasant, friendly demeanor and his adorable phobias, traits which endeared him to billions of fans across the globe. A memorial for Burbank will be held at his former home on Seahaven Island this Saturday in an internationally televised event that is expected to draw in billions of viewers and will likely be the most widely viewed television event in history.

A Joint Letter from the Member States of the African Union to Wakanda

To the Kingdom of Wakanda:

We, the other fifty-five member states of the African Union, write to you, first and foremost, to wish you our sincere condolences on the passing of your beloved king, T'Challa. He was a great ruler and our thoughts are with the Wakandan people in this time of grief. His loss will be mourned across our great continent.

In recent months, the Kingdom of Wakanda took radical steps to improve transparency and share its knowledge with other countries, and we praise your leaders for embracing a mindset of international cooperation rather than isolation—which is one of the primary goals of the African Union, after all. In doing so, Wakanda has revealed itself to be the most technologically advanced nation on the planet. Much to our surprise, we might add! Seriously, wow! Go Wakanda!

However, this newfound understanding of Wakanda's economic and technological status has also brought up a number of, let us say, discrepancies, that we feel we must address as we analyze Wakanda's past role within the African Union. We hate to burden the leadership of your great Kingdom with these inquiries during this difficult moment in your nation's history. But we would not be bringing these items to your attention if they were not of the utmost urgency.

Before we get into that, some history:

As you know, Wakanda was a founding member of the Organisation of African Unity, which was founded in 1963 to promote unity among African nations, facilitate international trade and technological exchange, defend national sovereignty, and, of course, eradicate colonialism and neo-colonialism on the continent. Nearly four decades later, the African Union replaced the OAF with broader and more ambitious goals, such as establishing a unified currency, a central bank, and open international borders.

King T'Challa—and King T'Chaka before him—both expressed a sincere interest in advancing the goals of the African Union, always saying things like, "Wakanda may be a nation of poor farmers, but we will do what we can!" In retrospect, we can imagine they must have had a good chuckle to themselves after saying that!

So, yes, Wakanda participated under the guise of being one of the poorest nations in Africa. But we think it's fair to say that Wakanda's contributions were fairly limited in scope considering your Kingdom has practically been living in the year 3000 with all of that vibranium technology you have.

Believe us, we get it. Not wanting to let powerful countries know you're sitting on the most valuable natural resource on Earth? You don't have to explain to us why you kept that under wraps. We're African countries. We know better than anywhere else on Earth what it's like to have all of your natural resources commandeered and extracted. So keeping it a secret and biding your time until you were ready to defend yourselves against the onslaught of powerful countries vying for a piece of that sweet, sweet vibranium? That makes perfect sense to us.

Nonetheless, learning about Wakanda's state-of-the-art military, cutting-edge medicine, and dazzling infrastructure has left us, the other members of the African Union, with some questions. So many questions. Questions like "What?" and "How?" and "Really? This whole time?"

So you can't fault us, your friendly African neighbors, for feeling like we kind of got played a little!

How long has Wakanda had vibranium weapons capable of stopping bullets, smashing vehicles, and launching your enemies into the air? Remember that time the Belgians completely destroyed the Congo? Or when the British did...well, pretty much what the British did everywhere, across half of Africa? Or the French? Or the Portuguese? Or the Germans? Or the Dutch? Or the Italians? Remember apartheid? Remember slavery? We could've used a couple of those vibranium staffs back then. Just saying! We know bringing up Killmogner is a bit of a sore spot among Wakandans. But you have to admit, the man had a point!

As for why the king of Wakanda would go gallivanting around as the Black Panther, fighting crime all around the world instead of helping his fellow Africans back home? Well, that is beyond us. Why would the Black Panther even want to be part of the Avengers? The Avengers are always fighting Thanos. Why do they never fight hunger? Or Malaria?

What really adds insult to injury, though, is the part where Wakanda posed as a poor country for decades. That really made us feel foolish. I mean, did you really have to apply for *loans* from the African Development Fund? Really? We get that you had to sell the grift of being impoverished. But come on. We all remember sitting through those presentations showing the "progress" Wakanda was making every time we lent you money. "Look! Wakanda built a road! Wakanda built a school! Wakanda has two traffic lights now!" we would all say with excitement as the Wakandan delegation reported their "evidence" of how the funds were being allocated. How stupid we must have looked to all of you! You tricky Wakandans, you!

Now we come to find that Wakanda's Sovereign Wealth Fund is eight times bigger than the entire ADF portfolio put together! Imagine that! And there we were scratching our heads wondering, "How is Wakanda going to pay back this $5 million bond to build their first water treatment plant?"

So, while this does explain how Wakanda managed to maintain a AAA credit rating, it suffices to say that we expect Wakanda to be more of a lender rather than a borrower from now on.

And don't even get us started on Wakanda's previous entries in our annual African Union Technology and Innovation Startup Incubator. You people had a vibranium-powered forcefield over your entire country, and you were purposefully phoning it in with pitches like "What if roads had lights so you could drive at night?" and "Fire, but inside a box with a door so you can cook stuff more easily." You assholes!

But, all of that aside, there's one major sticking point we need to address. Not to get too into the weeds here, but the African Union is funded through a 0.2 percent levy on imports from non-member states. It's a small tariff that helps fund the work of the African Union's many official bodies such as the Pan-African Parliament; the Economic, Social and Cultural Council; the African Commission on Human and Peoples' Rights; and the Africa Centres for Disease Control and Prevention.

Wakanda's average contribution under the agreement has been about $1.8 million per year, based on Wakanda's reported annual imports of $900 million. Now we come to find that Wakanda's imports are actually more like $900 *billion* a year, meaning Wakanda should have been paying $1.8 *billion* a year in dues. Bottom line is, Wakanda owes its African neighbors A LOT of money in financing dues. Dues that could have been paying for critical infrastructure, emergency preparedness, HIV drugs, vaccines, and more. "Wakanda Forever" better mean how often you people pay what you actually owe from now on.

And that's assuming we continue to ask Wakanda to fund the African Union at the same rate as other nations. Which, given that Wakanda's $6 trillion economy is more than ten times the size of any other African country's economy, seems like something that ought to be rethought as well.

Look, we're not asking for much. We're not asking for vibranium. And we're certainly not going to try to steal it. What do we look like, France?

It's just that, now that we know the world's most advanced economy has been right next door and pulling the wool over our eyes this entire time, we think it's time you pulled your weight around here on things like fighting disease, preventing famine, stopping war, and combating climate change (you've had fossil-fuel free energy this entire time? Come on!).

We're not asking for much, all we want is for the Black Panther and the warriors of Wakanda to spend a little less time fighting giant purple aliens and Mesoamerican merpeople, and a little more time helping their fellow African nations with the whole "not enough food and clean drinking water" thing. Because seriously, what the hell, Wakanda.

Love the new suit, though!

Sincerely,

ALGERIA, ANGOLA, BENIN, BOTSWANA, BURKINA FASO, BURUNDI, CAMEROON, CAPE VERDE, CENTRAL AFRICAN REPUBLIC, CHAD, COMOROS, DEMOCRATIC REPUBLIC OF THE CONGO, REPUBLIC OF THE CONGO, DJIBOUTI, EGYPT, EQUATORIAL GUINEA, ERITREA, ESWATINI, ETHIOPIA, GABON, GAMBIA, GHANA, GUINEA, GUINEA-BISSAU, CÔTE D'IVOIRE, KENYA, LESOTHO, LIBERIA, LIBYA, MADAGASCAR, MALAWI, MALI, MAURITANIA, MAURITIUS, MOROCCO, MOZAMBIQUE, NAMIBIA, NIGER, NIGERIA, RWANDA, SAHRAWI REPUBLIC, SÃO TOMÉ AND PRÍNCIPE, SENEGAL, SEYCHELLES, SIERRA LEONE, SOMALIA, SOUTH AFRICA, SOUTH SUDAN, SUDAN, TANZANIA, TOGO, TUNISIA, UGANDA, ZAMBIA, ZIMBABWE

Meanwhile, at the Regional Branch of a Major Credit Card Company...

— Good morning. I would like to apply for a credit card, please.

— Sure thing, just hand me those documents and I'll run a quick credit check...hmmm...let's see...I'm sorry, but it looks like your credit score is 410 and you are $278,000 in debt, so I'm afraid you're not eligible for credit with us.

— How is that possible?

— Well, looking at your credit history, it looks like you ran up a pretty big credit card bill with us, including charges for a $600 Hovetekke home exer-bike, a $500 sofa with Strinne green stripe pattern, and a $2,000 yin-yang coffee table. All of which, unfortunately, your insurance refused to cover because the fire department ruled your condo explosion an act of arson. More recently, it looks like there are charges totaling tens of thousands of dollars from an industrial chemical supplier. And it looks like you're also in default for a business loan for something called the "Paper Street Soap Company?" Oh, and the loan you used to cover the civil suit filed against you by "guest of the Pressman Hotel regarding the urine content of the lobster bisque." Any of that sound familiar?

— Sure, sure, but I meant, how do you still have those records if everybody's debt got erased last night?

— What?

— Yeah, after that guy blew up all of those credit card company headquarters, the debt record should've been erased so we'd all go back to zero. Total chaos.

— Oh, you mean that nutjob cult leader dude and his meathead buddies that punch each other for fun? What do they call themselves? Project Mayday or something?

— Project Mayhem. And I wouldn't call him a nutjob, more like an anti-consumerist visionary. Sure, he might've had some psychiatric issues, possibly an undiagnosed split personality disorder. But the primal thrill of bare-knuckle fighting can be very cathartic to lonely men who have been relegated to the margins of our materialistic, capitalist society. At least, that's what I've heard.

— Whatever he was trying to do, it didn't work.

— What do you mean?

— Well, sure, he blew up a couple corporate office buildings. But all those companies, including ours, keep their data backed up on server farms in, like, Finland or Norway—somewhere cold, all with multiple redundancies. You'd have to be a real dumbass not to realize that no bank is going to keep all of their data in one building with no backups anywhere else.

— Okay, well I'm sure whoever was behind Project Mayhem had plenty of good reasons to assume all of the data would be stored at the company headquarters. Like maybe he didn't know about the server farms because IT guys aren't exactly the type to join secret bare-knuckle boxing rings with strict rules, and maybe it was also really hard to recruit members in Europe because of the many language and cultural barriers.

— I guess so.

— So none of the data got destroyed?

— Nope.

— Huh.

— Is there anything else I can help you with today?

— You got any job openings?

A League of My Own

Dear Mr. Dugan,

My name is Rosa G. Cleavers, but my friends call me "Gigi." I wanted to try out for the American Girls Professional Baseball League last season, but was turned away because the league doesn't allow Black players. I guess it's not surprising coming from a league whose idea of "progress" involves making women wear skirts in a sport that involves sliding on dirt at full speed. Talk about a "rash" decision.

If you didn't notice me getting escorted out of the tryout, you might've seen me later just off the field at one of the Rockford Peaches games as they were warming up. I was the one who threw the ball back to your pitcher from just off the foul line in deep right field. Your catcher gave me a knowing look of game-recognize-game, but I couldn't stick around because I had to go back up into the stands and watch the ballgame from there. You know, on account of the whole not being able to play because I'm Black thing.

I'm writing to you because, with the new season coming up, I'm wondering if you might be willing to let me try out for the team and ask the league to rethink their policies about race. I realize you might not feel like sticking your neck out for me. Hell, you didn't even want this job in the first place. But I hope I can appeal to your competitive spirit as a guy who likes to win and will therefore do whatever it takes to get the best players on his team, regardless of the color of their skin, or how good they look doing the splits while catching a ball.

And why pick me? Well, for starters, a Black woman wouldn't skip the first six games of the World Series.

Look, I don't mean to cast aspersions on your players. But I'm sorry, leaving your team high and dry with the championship on the line? That's peak entitled white lady behavior. Even if you come back for game seven only to give up the game-winning run.

And sure, winning isn't everything. Sometimes seeing your sister gain the confidence in herself that she always lacked is a win in and of itself. But healing long-brewing sibling tensions is not why your players get paid to play baseball. Rest assured, complicated family drama is not going to be an issue with me. I have a sister who's also a heck of a ball player, but we don't squabble over who's in whose shadow. She and I have to stick together no matter what. Because we have bigger issues to deal with. Like how white people keep lighting our church on fire.

I'm not saying your players don't have real problems of their own. I can certainly sympathize with wanting to spend more time with your husband after he's just endured the horrors of war. My husband was in the war too. They stuck him and the other Black soldiers on the front lines. Where all the bullets and the grenades are. It's a miracle he survived. So God knows I'd love to spend every waking moment with him if I could.

But neither of us has been able to get a decent, high-paying job, so we both have to find whatever crappy minimum-wage gigs we can to make ends meet. And it'll be a while before we can save up to buy a house because every time my husband applies for one of those G.I. Bill mortgages, the forms get "lost in the mail." So needless to say, if you hire me, I'm not going to skip town right before a post-season showdown with our biggest rival. That's for damn sure.

As for your rule that "there's no crying in baseball," I happen to think shedding the occasional tear is a healthy way for any person, man or woman, athlete or not, to process their emotions. But, incidentally, I haven't cried since the time my husband and I didn't move off the sidewalk fast enough as a white woman was passing by and, the next day, the KKK threw a brick through our window. So occasionally getting yelled at by some drunk, washed-up ballplayer is not exactly going to faze me.

That said, all I'm asking is that you'll give me a chance. I know it's a long shot that the league will let me play given that "Canadians, Irish ones, and Swedes" is their idea of racial diversity. But I think it's worth a shot.

Lastly, for the sake of total transparency, you should know that I'll also have to bring my son along with me since, as I mentioned, my husband and I will both be working. But don't worry, he's extremely very well behaved. Letting your kid run up and down the aisle of a bus screaming and harassing the driver to the point where he nearly runs the bus off the road?

That's some white people shit.

It's High Time We Opened the Floodgates

I may just be a biker roaming around with my gang of outlaws everywhere from Gas Town to Bullet Farm in this every-person-for-themselves, post-apocalyptic desert hellscape. But I know when the wool is being pulled over my eyes. And there's no better example of wool pulling than the folks still trying to convince us that this barren wasteland we're living in now—where the only remaining civilization sits atop a tall mesa controlled by an army of blood-thirsty gasoline-obsessed freaks—was the result of human activity.

The people trying to convince us of this—typically a lone wanderer, or Vuvalini tribeswoman—are quick to point out that Earth once had a wide range of environmental habitats or "green places" until our overconsumption of resources led to all-out war, which led to the desolate landscape we see today.

Scientists claimed there was a causal link between humans blowing the planet to smithereens and the planet becoming a dry, inhospitable dystopia. But how can we really trust their theory that nuclear fallout caused the dense clouds that blocked out the sun for an entire year, thus killing virtually all plant life? Isn't it worth considering what they may have had to gain by trying to convince us that living on a planet choked by dense clouds of radioactive debris was a bad thing? Clearly they had an agenda. And I would ask one of them, but we already ate them all.

The Earth has had plenty of natural cycles between cold and hot, wet and dry. When I was a kid, there was a drought one summer and all of my mom's tomato plants died. Which was a huge bummer because the tomatoes that you used to be able to grow were way better than the ones you used to be able to buy at the store. Back when tomatoes and stores were a thing.

So it's possible that what we're experiencing—worldwide aridification where the only way to survive is to build elaborate war rigs and fight each other to the death while heavy metal music blares in the background—is just a temporary phenomenon. Maybe the world we're living in—where the only currency is fuel and the only rule is "survive"—will eventually swing back to the habitable planet days of old, and we can go back to using tons of gasoline and water the way we used to.

If anything, the real problem is leaders like Immortan Joe who refuse to open the floodgates to the reservoir inside the Citadel because we need to, in his words, "conserve water." It's these draconian, big-government warlord regulations that are the real reason nobody has enough to drink.

I propose we rid ourselves of those liquid-hogging goons and let individuals make their own decisions about how to use the water in the only remaining oasis for miles. Let's open the floodgates and take back what's rightfully ours! Only then can we end all this suffering while we wait for the planet to naturally become livable again.

It Turns Out Opening the Floodgates Was a Terrible Idea

So, I know earlier I had said that we should open the floodgates to the reservoir because Immortan Joe's onerous water regulations were the real problem. Well, I guess we found out the hard way that it wasn't such a good idea after all.

A few days ago, this renegade named Max and a warlord named Furiosa managed to kill Immortan Joe and lead a revolt against the War Boys. With Immortan Joe out of the picture, they opened the floodgates to the reservoir and the water came gushing out in a giant waterfall as the people celebrated being given unlimited access to the Citadel's resources. Finally, we had loosened the tight, bureaucratic grip the War Boys had held over the only reliable water supply for miles, ushering in the laissez-faire, unregulated approach to water management that we'd been calling for.

That was Thursday. By Sunday, things weren't looking so good.

At first, it was great having unlimited access to water. On Friday, a few of the bikers and I built a water slide at the edge of the falls and diverted some of the water into a makeshift lazy river we could float around in on old motorcycle tires. That was a blast.

By Saturday, the area around the falls started getting kind of mucky, but that ended up being a perfect spot for our Citadel-wide naked mud wrestling tournament where the winner got a year's supply of gasoline. That was also a ton of fun.

By Sunday, though, the falls were down to a trickle, and most of the water had either been absorbed into the ground, or flowed out into the desert, where it evaporated almost instantly.

That's when we realized we might've screwed the pooch on this one.

It turns out the War Boys had carefully engineered a system of aqueducts to deliver water to the few crops they were able to grow at the top of the Citadel. And any water that drained into the soil eventually made its way back down into the groundwater supply. This ensured that the water table underneath the Citadel remained relatively stable.

We had assumed they were just being assholes by not giving everyone unlimited access to the reservoir. But, in retrospect, letting anyone do whatever they wanted with the water supply wasn't a good idea in a place that only gets three inches of rainfall a year. Who knew?

I guess the moral of the story is, be careful what you wish for. That, and don't build waterparks in the desert.

But, oh well, now that our brief weekend of fun is over and we've descended back into an every-person-for-themselves, post-apocalyptic desert hellscape, I better get back to work. The gang and I have to get ready to raid Gas Town to see if we can scrounge up some food and water for the week. After that I'm not sure what we'll do. Hope that it rains soon, I guess?

Unfortunately, the Copyrights to Your Great-Great-Grandfather's Songs Are Actually Owned by a Complex Multinational Media Conglomerate

Hi Miguel,

Thank you for contacting Garselos, Tanaka, Adeoye & Smith. We pride ourselves on being the preeminent entertainment law firm across the globe with a long track record of delivering results for our clients in the areas of intellectual property, royalty, and contract law. Taylor Swift's re-recordings? That was our idea.

First of all, congratulations on successfully crossing over to the Land of the Dead and restoring your great-great-grandfather's musical legacy! It's so heartwarming that you were able to reconnect with him, heal a longstanding family feud, and share a tender moment with your great-grandmother before she passed away. I'm tearing up again just thinking about it!

It's totally understandable that, now that you know the truth about your great-great-grandfather and Ernesto De La Cruz, you'd want to set the record straight in the eyes of the law and get the copyrights to your great-great-grandfather's songs back into his name where they belong.

Unfortunately, it's a little more complicated than just filling out a couple forms. Because the copyrights to your great-great-grand-father's songs are actually owned by a complex multinational media conglomerate.

You, like most people, probably thought the music industry works like this: you write a song, you record the song, people buy recordings of the song, you make money.

But in reality it's more like this: you write a song, you perform the song in a dusty cabaret, an agent approaches you and says, "You've got what it takes to be a star, kid," you sign with the agent, the agent negotiates a contract with a record label, you license your song to the record label in exchange for a small advance, you record the song, the label negotiates a complex patchwork of contracts with various music distributors, broadcasting networks, and enter-tainment companies, and finally, if you're lucky, you earn royalties, assuming the label makes enough money for you to earn out your advance, *and* that your agent negotiated an airtight contract, *and* that your agent didn't screw you out of the royalties entirely.

Also bear in mind that Ernesto took all of your great-great-grand-father's songs and recorded them in the thirties, which was the wild west in terms of intellectual property law, both in the United States and Mexico. One of Ernesto's recording contracts that we were able to track down was handwritten in pen on a corn husk, and apparently that's still legally binding in the state of Guanajuato.

Here's the gist of what happened as far as we can tell. And please note that this does not constitute legal advice on the part of our firm, and we have not entered into a contract for legal services. But here goes:

In 1932, Ernesto started recording albums of your great-great-grandfather's songs for a small label in Michoacán. Then that label sold all of the rights to a bigger label in Mexico City, who then sold the rights to a Latin music distributor in Burbank, who then sold it back to a Mexican distributor in Guadalajara. Then we don't know what the hell happened because that distributor turned out to be a money-laundering front so their bookkeeping was pretty shoddy.

What we do know is that, over the years, the copyrights all somehow ended up in the hands of Fonovisa Records, which then got acquired by Universal Music Mexico, which is a subsidiary of Universal Music Latin Entertainment, which is a division of Universal Music Group N.V., which is headquartered in the Netherlands for some reason.

Incidentally, that means that, technically, every time you hear "Remember Me" on the radio, the Dutch government gets a tiny bit of tax revenue to pay for Dutch roads and Dutch bridges and textbooks for little Dutch kids. It's probably why the Dutch have free healthcare! All from a song your great-great-grandfather wrote for your great-grandmother in Santa Cecilia, Mexico in 1931. The global economy truly is a convoluted web of unfathomable intricacy.

The point is, not even Ernesto De La Cruz owned the songs he stole from your great-great-grandfather, so it would be a massive legal undertaking to try to get the rights back. And although your great-great-grandfather may own the rights to those songs in the court of public opinion, that's not going to hold up in actual court.

Sadly, the only way to actually get the copyrights to your great-great-grandfather's music would be to sue Universal Music. And have you tried suing a major corporation lately? It would take a lifetime of busking in the plaza just to afford all the necessary court filings. So even if you were successful, it's unlikely you'd come out ahead financially. Last year, Ernesto De La Cruz's recordings of your great-great-grandfather's songs were played 208 million times on Spotify, 133 million times on Amazon Music, and 112 million times on Apple Music. Which works out to a total of $92.14 in royalty payments. And bear in mind, he's in the top 5 percent of artists in terms of streaming revenue. So there's not a ton of damages you'd be entitled to as a plaintiff. Your parents aren't exactly crazy for having reservations about your desire to pursue a career in music.

Our personal advice (again this does not constitute legal advice on the part of our firm, just to be totally clear) is this: Enjoy playing your great-great-grandfather's songs with your family. Enjoy his restored reputation around town. And if you ever decided to record your own music, consider distributing the albums on an independent, creator-owned platform where you retain full rights.

Alternatively, have you thought about re-recording his songs as English-Spanish pop-reggaeton crossovers? That's where the real money is these days.

Sincerely,
Vera C. Garselos, Esq.
Garselos, Tanaka, Adeoye &
Smith, LLP

Legal Notice:

This message is being sent by or on behalf of a lawyer. It is intended exclusively for the individual or entity to which it is addressed. This communication may contain information that is proprietary, privileged or confidential or otherwise legally exempt from disclosure. This communication may, but does not necessarily constitute legal advice on the part of Garselos, Tanaka, Adeoye & Smith, LLP and should not be taken to constitute legal services unless a written agreement for legal services has been entered into by the client.

Meanwhile, Somewhere in Venezuela...

— *Comandante*, there's something you should see.

— What is it, *Capitán*?

— Radar picked up a bogey entering our airspace at an altitude of 6,000 feet and traveling south at ten kilometers per hour. No registered flight path.

— Ten kilometers an hour? What is it, some sort of stray weather balloon?

— It's a house.

— A house??

— Yes, a *Yanqui* house by the looks of it. With a couple thousand helium balloons attached to it.

— You've got to be kidding.

— No, I swear, it's real. Recon did a fly-by and captured footage. Look.

— Good lord. Have you tried to radio them?

— We did, but no response. We did confirm it's occupied, though.

— By who?

— An old man and a boy scout. And a dog.

— Of course they brought a dog. What's their trajectory?

— They're heading for the high-altitude rainforest.

— Son of a bitch. Please tell me they're not...

— Heading to the area with the endangered birds? The birds our ecologists have been carefully monitoring from afar for years so as not to disturb their natural habitat? And have kept the location of their nesting grounds secret in order to protect them from poachers and "explorers" hunting them to extinction? Yep, they're heading straight there.

— Jesus Christ. Is there any way we can intercept them?

— We don't have any aircraft that can move that slowly.

— Shit.

• • •

— An entire house lifted by balloons? Goddamn Americans.

— Goddamn Americans, indeed, *Comandante*.

A Message from
SOYLENT FARMS
to
OUR CUSTOMERS

There are plenty of options when it comes to food. Well, not plenty, but at least two. The point is, we understand the importance of earning your business. That's why we here at Soylent Farms are committed to providing you with the most satisfying eating experience on the market. Our signature product, Soylent Green, has been the leading food wafer brand since 2123 for one simple reason: Because here at Soylent Farms, we believe that food should be made by people, for people, of people.

Soylent Farms began as a passion project started by two college roommates. Pete and Cam saw a problem: Anthropogenic climate change was causing massive worldwide food shortages, and overcrowded cities were quickly descending into widespread civil unrest. So they thought, why not kill two birds with one stone? Or, as they like to say, "Why not feed two birds with one scone that's also made of bird?"

One bathtub, and a few household chemicals later, Soylent Farms was born. Their operation started off small—luring the occasional drifter into their apartment and dissolving them in the tub using their patented cocktail of naturally derived solvents. Then adding their signature blend of herbs and spices, separating the batter into bite-sized wafers, and baking them for just the right amount of time to get that perfect Soylent Green crunch that our customers have come to love.

From those humble beginnings, Soylent Farms eventually grew into the largest food provider in North America, thanks to our talented, dedicated employees, and our strategic partnerships with state and local population control agencies. But we've never forgotten our roots. That's why every batch of Soylent Green is still hand-crafted by our team of expert waferologists to ensure that each box of Soylent Green contains only the most nutritious, most delicious wafers.

We also use only the very best ingredients in our product. That's right, no stockbrokers, ska musicians, or people named Brett. Other brands of food wafer might, but not us. The only people you'll ever find in a box of Soylent Green are middle school math teachers, hospice nurses, and public defenders. That's it.

We also believe that, before people are turned into industrial food paste, they deserve to be treated with respect. That's why all of our people are cage-free, cruelty-free, and fed a certified organic diet. Once they arrive at our facility, each and every one of the people that ends up in a Soylent Green wafer is treated to a premium comfort experience, complete with a relaxing hot tub soak, followed by an erotic massage from one of our trained sexbots. Then they're given a strong cocktail of Benzodiazepine and MDMA, so that each person is dumped into our giant bone-separating machine feeling happy as a clam. Other brands wouldn't go to such lengths to ensure people are melted into processed food products with dignity. That's what makes us different.

So the next time you reach for a box of food wafers at your local grocery store or government-designated fallout shelter, remember: *If it's made by machine, it ain't Soylent Green.* Enjoy!

Sincerely,

Pete LaPeroe

Pete LaPeroe

Cam Linnaban

Cam Linnaban

A Favor You Can't Refuse

Bona sera, tutti, and thank you all for coming to celebrate the wedding of my wonderful daughter, Connie. My wife Carmela and I could not have asked for a better day, and we are truly blessed to be surrounded by so many cherished family members and friends, including my godson, Johnny Fontane, who came all the way from Hollywood to be here today. And of course, my son Michael, who just returned from his service in the Marines.

Connie will always be my little girl, and it's been one of the great joys of my life watching her grow into the strong, intelligent, beautiful woman she is today. I remember when Connie was little, she used to do this thing where she'd...hang on a second, my colleague Luca Brasi is waving at me to come to the office, which can only mean one thing...excuse me...

Actually, you know what, *basta.* Let me say something about this little "tradition." As you all know, it is Sicilian custom that the father of the bride cannot refuse a favor on the day of his daughter's wedding. And some of you good-for-nothings have taken this way too far. I've spent practically the entire day in my dimly lit office

listening to your requests instead of out here drinking and celebrating as I should be. I barely had time to squeeze in a single dance
with my daughter before I had to run back to the office and deal
with more of your ridiculous pleas.

So, as much as I'm a man who respects tradition, enough with
the favors!

Don't get me wrong, as a pillar of the community, I'm happy to
do the occasional favor for a friend. All I ask is that one day—and
this day may never come—I may call upon you to return the favor.
Which is a pretty fair trade, if you ask me.

And I pride myself on being the person you can count on in your
hour of need. Avenging your daughter because the American criminal justice system refuses to hold men accountable for sexual as-
sault? Simple. I tell Clemenza to get some guys together (who aren't
gonna get too carried away) and have them break a few kneecaps.

Trying to make it as an actor? Piece of cake. I send Hagen to talk
to the studio head, and if he refuses to play ball, we give him a little
"wake-up call" so he changes his mind. A struggling actor gets his
big break and an arrogant Hollywood executive gets taken down a
peg. Win-win.

If only all favors were that simple! I've had people coming out of
the woodwork for all sorts of things. A cousin wants a loan to open
an Italian bakery in Chinatown (it'll break my heart to collect when
that fails). A neighbor wants me to help him open a picture-framing
store (no, not a money laundering one, a real one! A real one!). And,
next week, I have to go to a party on Arthur Avenue because my
friend wants to go, but he only knows the host, and he doesn't want
to show up, and then the host is busy talking to someone else, and
everyone else has already formed a conversation circle, so he has to
stand awkwardly near one of the circles and wait until someone

says something where there's a natural point to jump in. Can you believe it? Imagine me, Don Corleone, notorious head of the Corleone family, somebody's wingman? You show me such disrespect, on this, the day my daughter is to be wed in holy matrimony?

It's one thing to ask me to be the godfather of your child. I'm already godfather to seventy-two children, what's one more? But to come to me on a sacred day like today and ask if I can pick up your dry-cleaning because you're going to be out of town for a couple days? I mean, where does it end? It would be one thing if I could dump that favor onto one of my trusted associates, but Clemenza's going to be away on a job, and Luca Brasi has a "thing." So now I'm going to be the one stuck doing it. And I did not come all the way over from Sicily just to carry around some goomba's dirty underwear.

The real kicker is, nobody even knows where this ridiculous tradition started! Some say it goes all the way back to the fifteenth century when, legend has it, the King of Sicily was so elated during the day of his daughter's wedding that he granted his entire court one favor of their choosing. Others say it goes further back to one of the Emirs of Sicily during the Arab conquest of the ninth century. And some claim it was just something the Sicilians made up in the early 1900s because we Sicilians love any excuse to barter with favors instead of currency. Either way, it's gotten totally out of control.

People assume that, as The Godfather, my life is all take and no give. But I do things for people all the time. I give people good jobs. I help people get their businesses off the ground. And when those businesses are under threat of violence and intimidation, I offer protection. Sure, sometimes I'm the one threatening the violence, but generating demand for your products is what every business in America does in one way or another.

My point is, even The Godfather can only do so much. The night is almost over, and there are still people coming to me to ask for a meeting. I know some of those favors will be easy, like taking relatives who are a liability to the family out for a "fishing trip on the lake." And some will be difficult, like cat-sitting for my niece Natalia (I love cats, but I hate taking the ferry to Staten Island). Either way, they're more than any one man should have to handle.

So for those of you who haven't yet called upon me this evening, I say: eat, dance, sing, and enjoy this special night. But please, no more favors. Or else.

But that's enough about me, we've got a wedding to celebrate. I forgot where I had left off, and I've been up here long enough, so let me just wrap this up. All I wanted to say was a quick toast to the happy couple.

To Connie, my sweetest little angel, who every day makes me want to be a better man. And to Carlo, the guy she's marrying.

Salute!

United States Patent

Heald et al.

Patent No. 7,534,829

Date of Patent: Mar. 26, 2010

HOT TUB TIME MACHINE

Applicant: **Metro-Goldwyn-Mayer Studios, Inc.**, Beverly Hills, CA (US)

Inventor: **Josh Heald, Sean Anders, John Morris,** Los Angeles, CA (US)

Appl. No.: **12/102,346**

Filed: **May 8, 2009**

References Cited

U.S. PATENT DOCUMENTS

38,655	1/1895	Wells
4,123,456	11/1963	Who et al.
5,473,322	7/1985	Brown
5,548,380	2/1989	Bill, Ted, et al.
5,845,284	6/1992	McGonagall
5,920,923	7/1999	Jillette
8,283,938	4/2019	Banner, Stark, et al.
8,453,265	8/2020	Nolan
11,300,297	4/2022	Hatley
11,319,721	5/2022	Schroeder
33,576,898	3/2029	Cyberdyne A.I.

ABSTRACT

There are many types of time machines of various sizes and form factors, each of which is suited to different applications. Examples include U.S. Patent No. 4,123,456 "Police Box 'TARDIS' Time Machine," Who et al., which is designed to blend into the London cityscape; U.S. Patent No. 5,473,322 "DeLorean Time Machine," Brown, which is designed to travel through time once a speed of 88mph has been achieved; and U.S. Patent No 33,576,898 "Skynet Time Travel Portal," Cyberdyne A.I., which is designed to send cyborg assassins back in time to murder the future savior of humanity.

There are also many types of hot tubs suited to various needs, including U.S. Patent No. 11,319,721 "Portable Hot Tub," Schroeder, a hot tub that can be hitched to the back of a vehicle and transported easily; U.S. Patent No.

11,300,297 "Fire Fixture For Hot Tub," Hatley, a hot tub with a functional fire pit in the middle; and U.S. Patent No. 5,920,923 "Hydro-Therapeutic Stimulator," Jillette, a hot tub specifically designed for clitoral stimulation.

But, though there are many types of time machines and many types of hot tubs, there has never been a time machine that is also a hot tub.

BACKGROUND OF THE INVENTION

From the very first time machine (U.S. Patent No. 38,655 "Time Machine," Wells), time travel has provided a means for humankind to traverse space-time in a non-linear fashion in order to experience both past and future time. This ability has been employed for a multitude of purposes ranging from getting an "A" on a history project (U.S. Patent No. 5,548,380 "American Telephone Booth Time Machine," Bill, Ted, et al.), to preventing half of all known life in the universe from being spontaneously eradicated at the snap of a finger (U.S. Patent No. 8,283,938 "Avengers Time Machine," Banner, Stark et al.)

However, the ability to traverse space-time while also comfortably seated in a bath of hot, bubbling water has not, prior to this filing, been achieved. This novel method of temporal travel offers several advantages over existing methods, such as soothing the user in order to make jumping through time less nauseating, as well as allowing the user to comfortably travel through time in otherwise unforgivingly cold temperatures such as on the back deck of a ski lodge during the winter in the American Mountain West.

SUMMARY OF THE INVENTION
TUB:

The Hot Tub Time Machine consists of a standard circular fiberglass tub, 6' in diameter, with 16 jacuzzi jets with a flow rate of 100 cubic feet per minute. **FIG 1**

DISPLAY PANEL:

Most time machines have a panel prominently located that displays important settings such as date and time of destination, velocity, fuel level, and other attributes to aid in getting to the desired point in time.

This time machine, on the other hand, has no labeled buttons whatsoever, and the only time setting can easily be confused for temperature or jet intensity to an untrained operator. This novel display panel is intentionally ambiguous and difficult to operate in order to encourage the user to be subjected to misadventurous screwball hijinx. **FIG 2**

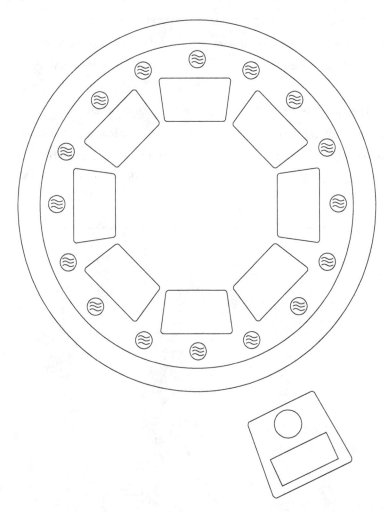

Fig. 1

TIME TRAVEL METHOD:

A standard GE 362 Time Engine is the primary device used for time travel. The time travel engine sits directly underneath the display panel. The Time Engine has been modified for this specific application using an additional temporal paradox avoidance circuit.

FUEL:

The Hot Tub Time Machine is the first of its kind to be powered by nitratriminium-based fuel poured directly over the display panel. **FIG 3**

CLAIMS

What is claimed is:

1. A time machine that is also a hot tub.

2. A time machine that is also a hot tub according to claim 1 that is powered exclusively from standard 120 VAC and Russian energy drinks.

3. A time machine that is also a hot tub according to claim 1 that is set to 1986 by default.

4. A time machine that is also a hot tub according to claim 1 that will send the user(s) back into their

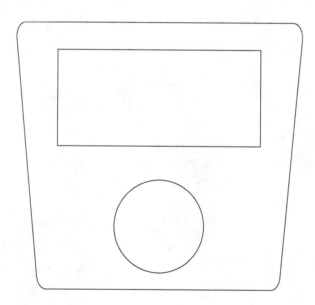

Fig. 2

Fig. 3

same bodies in order to avoid running into previous versions of themselves, thereby creating a temporal paradox (see U.S. Patent No. 5,845,284 "Time-Turner," McGonagall, U.S. Patent No. 8,453,265 "Time Inverter," Nolan).

5. A time machine that is also a hot tub according to claim 1 that is functional whether the user is fully clothed, partially clothed, or fully naked.

6. A time machine that can only be repaired by a mysterious elderly technician who seemingly appears out of nowhere and whose origin story is never explained.

7. A time machine that is also a hot tub according to claim 1 that emits a soothing amber glow to

notify the user that the time-travel function is operational.

8. A time machine that is also a hot tub according to claim 1 with AMH pulsator jacuzzi jets for maximum comfort when traveling through time.

9. A time machine that is also a hot tub according to claim 1 that may cause the user to accidentally walk in on their parents conceiving them.

10. A time machine that is also a hot tub according to claim 1 that, even when the time travel element is not functioning properly, is still a very good hot tub.

Meanwhile, Back in the Future...

— Hey, Marty!

— Oh, hey, Mr. Mayor!

— Nice car you got there!

— Thanks! Funny story, it's actually a time machine. I accidentally went back in time to 1955 and almost erased myself from existence! But it's all good now. In fact, our family is materially way better off than we were before, so I guess we really lucked out! Man, 1955 sure was heavy!

— Ah, cool, cool. Hey Marty, quick question. When you went back in time and supposedly "fixed" everything, you didn't by any chance do anything to combat, oh I don't know, racism?

— I hadn't thought about that!

— Uh uh. See, it's funny, 'cause I was around in 1955 and I guess
you could say it was "heavy." If by heavy you mean the fact that
I had to sweep the floors and scrub the toilets at Lou's Cafe for
75 cents an hour 'cause that was the only job I could get in
town. Do you have any idea how hard it is clawing your way up
from being a busboy, to a waiter, to a manager, to opening your
own restaurant, to finally being elected mayor? But you wanna
know what the real kicker is? I still can't get a single damn
rezoning bill passed 'cause the city council thinks building
affordable housing downtown could "ruin the town's charm."
And don't even get me started on police reform. So, yeah, I
guess if someone had the almighty power to travel through
time, you'd hope they might try to do something about that.
Hell, while they're at it they ought to go back to 1885 and
prevent the Pohatchees from being displaced too. Or go back to
1625 and prevent, just spitballing here, the African slave trade?
'Cause it sure would be a shame to have the ability to change
things for the better, and do nothing, so that thirty years from
now, in 2015, the only societal advantages we'll have are sixteen
more Jaws movies, hoverboards, and Nike shoes that lace
themselves. But, hey, that's just me.

— Oh, one other thing I forgot to tell you! You'll get a kick out of
this. I played "Johnny B. Goode" for everyone at my mom's high
school and they loved it! So I copyrighted the song and licensed
it to Chuck Berry. And now, anytime the song plays, I get
money! Isn't that neat?

— Wonderful, just wonderful. Oh, by the way, the sheriff clocked a
car that looked just like this one doing 88 in a 35 in the middle

of downtown. But I told him to look the other way, 'cause I thought to myself, "I know Marty's a good kid." And that's what good neighbors do for each other, right? They look out for one another. And they use whatever tools they have at their disposal for the good of their community. You get what I'm saying?

— Thanks, daddy-o! You're the best. Well, gotta run. I'm gonna go push Biff into a manure truck. It'll be hilarious!

— Is that a Rolex you got on, Marty? What a lovely watch. Just beautiful...

United States Department of the Interior
NATIONAL PARK SERVICE
GRAND CANYON NATIONAL PARK
20 S Entrance Road
Grand Canyon Village, Arizona 86023

Public Service Announcement:
Do Not Launch Your Car Headlong into the Grand Canyon

The Grand Canyon is one of the greatest natural wonders of the world, and, as the National Park service, it's our job to keep it that way. That means protecting the canyon walls from erosion, preventing tourists from climbing delicate rock formations, removing graffiti, and, of course, keeping the park as free of trash and debris as possible. So, for the love of God, do not launch your car headlong into the Grand Canyon.

Taking care of Grand Canyon National Park is no easy feat. The Grand Canyon is 277 miles long and up to 18 miles wide, with steep walls and an average depth of roughly a mile. The vast size and remoteness of the canyon make certain sections of the park difficult to access. So when a classic convertible—along with its folk hero passengers—soars off the edge of the canyon and smashes to pieces on the rocks below, it's a tricky mess for the park service to clean up. The last thing a National Park ranger wants to do is spend eight hours in the punishing Arizona sun riding a donkey along a sheer cliff face just so they can peel your mangled body parts off of a cactus with one of those long, trash grabber tools. So maybe think about that before committing suicide-by-vehicle while running from the law?

In addition to its natural beauty, the Grand Canyon is also an ecologically sensitive area with a mix of ponderosa pine, desert scrub, and riparian ecosystems, all of which are highly susceptible to environmental pollution. A single 1966 Ford Thunderbird contains over fifty chemicals known to be highly toxic to plant and animal life. So it should go without saying that having loose T-Bird parts strewn across the slopes of the canyon presents a serious risk to the local flora and fauna. And that's to say nothing about the danger posed to the Grand Canyon's most endangered species, *Astragalus cremnophylax*. The tiny shrub, found only along the rim of the Grand Canyon, is highly sensitive to being trampled by the occasional wandering tourist, let alone by the tires of a 3,500-pound vintage drop-top as it flies off the edge of the cliff wall with two feminist legends inside.

Look, we get it. Going airborne over the quintessential geological feature of the American Southwest looks really cool. Some might even say iconic. And there's no question that the patriarchy has pushed many a woman to the brink of a precipice, metaphorical or literal. But a few poster-worthy seconds of stick-it-to-the-man, mid-air awesomeness is hardly worth all of the effort required to deal with the aftermath. Park rangers spend 99 percent of their working lives yelling at kids to stop running so they don't trip and fall to their deaths, and constantly emptying overflowing garbage cans full of half-eaten ice cream before the bears eat it all and die of diabetes. It's a thankless enough job as it is without having to deal with twisted-up automotive parts and human remains halfway up the sides of Horseshoe Bend. Especially when carcass removal doesn't even qualify as overtime.

So please think twice before driving your vehicle over the rust-colored strata of the Grand Canyon into the abyss below. And if you absolutely must fling yourself into the canyon, at least do it on foot and not in a car. People taking selfies too close to the edge fall in all the time, but they're a lot easier to clean up.

Sincerely,

Cora Sergalves
Director, Grand Canyon National Park

We're the Public School Next to Welton Academy and We'll Gladly Take Any Textbooks the Dead Poets Society Doesn't Want

When we first heard that students at Welton Academy were being taught by an eccentric, poetry-obsessed alumnus, we couldn't have been happier for them. Teaching the next generation of doctors, lawyers, and bankers how to get in touch with their emotional side in order to become more compassionate adults is a much-needed pedagogical shift in this country.

But, speaking of compassion, we couldn't help but notice that your new teacher's very first lesson involved ripping pages out of a perfectly good poetry textbook shortly after ranting about how his students needed to "seize the day" before they became "food for worms."

Well, we just want to say that, as the public high school next door, we'll gladly take any textbooks you Welton folks don't want.

To state the obvious—our schools are not exactly on a level playing field. It's great that Welton sends 75 percent of your students to the Ivy League, but we're lucky if we get 75 percent of our students to graduate. So while you're teaching your kids to *carpe diem*, we're just happy if our kids *carpe diploma* by the time they turn nineteen.

Welton Academy can no doubt afford to give every incoming junior a copy of J. Evans Pritchard's *Understanding Poetry* only to have them tear it to pieces as an exercise in thinking for themselves the way their teacher told them to. Meanwhile, over at our school, all of our copies of *A Midsummer Night's Dream* were eaten by moths over the summer, so we have to share the one remaining, tattered copy between six sophomore English classes. You folks can let poetry drip down your tongues like honey all you want. We just want poetry that isn't dripping with some sort of mystery fluid from our leaky HVAC system.

Graphing the perfection vs. importance of poems might be an unnecessarily mathematical way to assess their merit. And there are probably plenty of better textbooks for appreciating poetry. But good poetry textbooks are expensive. To put things in context, your school's uniforms were made by Brooks Brothers. Our football team's uniforms were handsewn by Brooke's brother—the brother of our cheerleading captain, Brooke, who works part time at a place that does dress alterations. So it's safe to say we are not a school that has fancy poetry textbook kind of cash. We will therefore gladly take any free books we can get our hands on, and we are not above taping torn out pages back in ourselves if we have to.

If we haven't made it clear yet, we're really not that picky. Most of our students' knowledge of poetry starts and ends with the bawdy limericks they read in *Playboy*. So any literary analysis we can expose them to, pedantic or not, is a pretty big win for us. And if we're being honest, while you're teaching your students to be the free-thinking leaders of tomorrow, our primary goal is just to make sure that our students leave high school with the basic reading comprehension skills they'll need to hold down a decent job and do their taxes. Whatever language skills the average plumber needs is roughly the bar we're aiming for here.

The biggest disciplinary issue at Welton is a couple of boys sneaking off to a cave to play the saxophone and give racially insensitive poetry readings. Our students, by comparison, sneak off to that same cave to play "hide the salami" and give each other HPV. You have a "Dead Poets Society" because it's fun. We have a "Teen Parents Society" because the state doesn't let us talk about birth control in health class. Do you see where we're coming from?

The point is, if your faculty members want to quote Walt Whitman and tell their students that "words and ideas can change the world," that's fine. And if your faculty members want to inspire students to the point where they start jumping up on their desks shouting, "Oh captain, my captain!" That's fine too. But, if they're going to do that, the least they can do is make sure that any teaching material they choose to discard along the way is preserved so that it can be sent over to our school down the street, where black mold has been growing on the ceiling of our gym since the late forties because we can't afford a tall enough ladder to reach it.

On a related note, we heard about the new English teacher getting let go. Do you think he'd be willing to work at our school for a third of his previous salary? If it's any consolation to him, he would be our highest paid employee.

The Shawshank Infection

Dear Red,

If you're reading this, you've gotten out. And if you've come this far, maybe you're willing to come a little further. You remember the name of the town, don't you? I could use a good man to help me get my project on wheels. I'll keep an eye out for you and the chessboard ready. Remember, Red, hope is a good thing, maybe the best of things, and no good thing ever dies. I will be hoping that this letter finds you, and finds you well.

Your friend,
Andy

P.S. There's more on the reverse side of this paper as well as a few additional sheets I've attached. Let's just say, there have been some new developments since I wrote that first part.

Okay, strap in, Red, because when I wrote that first letter, I was an entirely different man. I hadn't seen what I've seen. Been through what I've been through. So find a good sturdy rock and get comfortable, because you're going to want to be sitting for this.

You probably know by now how I managed to get out of Shawshank—the Raquel Welch poster, the old rock hammer, carrying the dirt out to the yard one handful at a time, climbing down to the sewer pipe, crawling through it, emerging in the pouring rain, ripping my shirt off, looking up triumphantly. I guess you couldn't have known about that last part, but it's not difficult to imagine.

Anyway, you also likely heard about how I cashed in all that laundered, "Randall Stephens" money, then mailed the ledger and all the other evidence of corruption at Shawshank over to the local paper. Was it badass? Vindicating? A feel good ending? Heck yeah.

But that's just the half of it. You see, after I finished closing out the last bank account, I caught the Greyhound over to Buxton to bury that tin box you dug up just now, and started writing the first part of this letter—the part about hope and the chessboard and all that sentimental crap.

That's when the gurgling started.

You see, here's the thing about crawling through five hundred yards of shit-smelling foulness on your way to freedom. Yes, the smell is unbearable. Yes, I vomited multiple times. Yes, I was lucky my little bundle of clothing and paperwork tied to my leg never came undone. And yes, it's a miracle all the hydrogen sulfide, methane, and ammonia trapped in the pipe didn't kill me. I had you smuggle in soapstone and alabaster to carve a chess set when I should've asked you to smuggle in a hazmat suit. Chalk it up to hindsight being 20/20 and whatnot.

But stench and toxic gas aside, there's another big problem with crawling through a half mile of raw sewage on your hands and knees. Germs.

The thing about bacteria is—no matter how hard you scrub yourself off in the rain afterwards—if you wade through a breeding ground for trillions upon trillions of microbes, you're going to end up getting some of them in your system. It's inevitable.

And the collective piss and shit produced by a prison—full of guys eating questionably prepared food—all flowing through one big drain pipe? That's an ecosystem with some nasty pathogens.

The first sickness to hit was (I'm guessing) salmonella. But honestly, it could have been any stomach bug. This was your typical, non-stop-liquid-out-both-ends-for-a-couple-days gastrointestinal illness.

That one hit right as I was heading to Buxton. And let me tell you, I was hanging on for dear life on that bus. This was not a fancy Greyhound with a bathroom in the back. This was one of those old-school, metallic exterior Greyhounds they still use in all the Podunk towns. That bus ride was the longest forty minutes of my life. And you and I both know I've had some forty-minute stretches in Shawshank that felt like a long-ass time.

So, the bus pulls into Buxton, I wrestle my way past every other person on that coach, locate the nearest diner, hit the head, and proceed to blow up their toilet like it's the Germans rolling into Leningrad. I'm talking, this toilet is *ruined*.

An hour later, I limp out of there, tail between my legs, and order a coffee and a chicken noodle soup, to go, because I know if I stay there for another ten minutes it's going to be WWIII in the men's room and I've already made enough of a mess.

Now I have a difficult decision to make. I know whatever I'm coming down with, I'm going to feel like absolute death for the next three to five days. And it won't be long before the Shawshank Search Brigade starts putting up flyers and running TV ads with yours truly's face on them, so time is not exactly on my side.

I could go to a doctor's office and try to get some meds to nip this thing in the bud. But that carries its own set of risks, because any place I have to flash Randall Stephens's forged ID around, is one more place I could get busted and sent back to Shawshank.

I figure I can't risk it, and decide I have to hunker down as best I can and ride this thing out. So I look around town for the sleaziest motel I can find—the kind where they don't want to ask questions about you any more than you want to ask questions about them—and hope for the best.

I find a place, get a room, ignore the questionable smell of the sheets (I'm in no position to be picky), hunker down, and try to get some sleep in between frantic runs to the toilet—a toilet that, try as it might, ends up being no match for my bowels. So if you ever find yourself staying in room 203 of the Lonely Pine Motel in Buxton, DO NOT use the ice bucket. I'll just leave it at that.

Meanwhile, back at the ranch, the Shawshank Goon Squad has likely found the tunnel by now, assembled a search party, and has bloodhounds searching the area around the prison. Also, the paper has probably just sent off their "Corruption at Shawshank" front page story to the printer, so this place is going to be swarming with journalists in about twenty-four hours. Things are not looking good for your pal Andy right now.

The next morning, I open my eyes and, no matter how hard I try, I cannot get myself out of bed. This time period is what I'm calling the "fever dream phase" of my ailment. I don't know if it's still the stomach bug that's causing it, or if I've come down with full-blown Hep A, Typhoid, or a microbe cocktail of bacteria and viruses kicking my ass all at once. Either way, by this point, I'm running the most intense fever I have experienced in my life. The entire day, I'm oscillating between lying buck naked on the floor of the bathroom dabbing cold water on myself, and wrapping myself as tightly as I can in the gross hotel sheets because I'm shivering convulsively like a dog that just got out of the bath.

When I do manage to drift off to sleep, I have vivid hallucinations, like one where Raquel Welch and I are dressed in bodysuits, *Fantastic Voyage* style. We shoot at all the bacteria around us with powerful, germ-killing lasers, and once they're all dead, we make sweet love on top of a red blood cell. Then I wake up soaked in sweat and it's time for another session on the cool tile of the bathroom floor.

The corruption story has definitely broken by now and Norton has probably put a bullet through the back of his brain. So, yeah, "His judgment cometh, and that right soon." Meanwhile, "My river runneth, in this motel bathroom." Bad news for me, considering the Maine State Police are still on the lookout for Shawshank's notorious escape artist. Innocent or not, I don't exactly feel like leaving my fate in the hands of the Maine criminal justice system again.

But, as much as I'd like to hightail it outta there, by this point I'm passed out and dreaming about clapping thighs with Golden Globe–winning actress and international sex symbol Raquel Welch, who has now transformed into a half-woman half-amoeba chimera, although I'm still weirdly into it.

By the third day, I can stand on my own two feet again, which feels nothing short of miraculous. I even manage to hold down the chicken noodle soup from the other day (thank God for the mini fridge and microwave in the room, even if the staff hasn't cleaned them once since they were purchased).

Now I'm at a crossroads: I'm well enough that I can get myself to a clinic and get medical care, which seems like the responsible thing to do given my state. I'm speculating whether I can get treated and get on my way before they ask for my paperwork, or if I'll be turned away at the door. Having spent the last two decades locked up, I don't exactly remember how health insurance works.

That's when it occurs to me that I'd better turn on the TV and get a sense for the situation out there. Sure enough, on channel five, it's exclusive coverage of the "Jailbreak at Shawshank." There's a reporter standing in the grass outside the prison right above where the sewage pipe empties out into the drainage ditch. In the top right corner of the screen above his head is my mugshot from 1947 in all its black-and-white glory. So that rules out a hospital visit.

Which is a bummer, because, by day three, I notice the flesh-eating bacteria are doing a number on my hand.

You see, the problem with army-crawling through five football fields of human waste is that there's no way to avoid your hands coming into contact with a whole lot of contaminated water. And when you're dragging your entire body by your hands along a sixty-year-old clay pipe, you're bound to get some scratches and scrapes along the way. So you can imagine that, no matter how hard you scrub your hands, the second you spill out of the pipe and into the drainage ditch, there's just no way to avoid collecting some infectious hitchhikers on those shit-covered paws of yours.

So, yeah, my hands are bloody, blistered, and severely discolored.

Who's about to have zero thumbs and a rapidly worsening case of gangrene? This guy.

Not being able to gesture approval or disapproval is hardly my biggest worry, though, because I've got to get the hell out of Maine if I'm ever going to make it to Mexico before Border Patrol can clock me on my way across the Rio Grande.

I check out of the motel (no questions asked) and walk over to the road to flash the international hand signal for needing a ride somewhere (while I still have the thumbs to do it). That's when I remember that I've still got one thing to take care of while I'm in Buxton—the entire reason I'm there in the first place.

I amble down Route 202, doing my best not to make eye contact with any of the cars as they pass by, and duck into a corn field as soon as I'm out of town, figuring my best bet is to cut through as much farmland as I can to minimize being spotted.

Finally, I make it to this very spot, the one I told you about before I left, and start digging. Which, as you can imagine, is excruciatingly painful on account of the bacteria in the process of devouring my digits.

I finish digging the hole, pull out the letter I'd written a few days ago, and give it a quick read.

How naïve I sounded just three short days ago! How unbridled my enthusiasm was! How optimistic that I'd hatched an infallible plan and would be on my way to the Mexican Riviera before anyone even knew I was gone!

That said, a couple things:

First, the name of the town is Zihuatanejo! Zi-hua-ta-ne-jo. It's in the state of Guerrero, on the Pacific coast. I can't believe I was going to leave it up to chance that'd you'd remember the name of an obscure, non-intuitively named Mexican village that I mentioned to you in passing one time, like, ten years ago. That's absurd! That's the thinking of a man who finally got justice and feels on top of the world. Not the thinking of a man who just spent the last seventy-two hours wishing for a quick and merciful death. Zi-hua-ta-ne-jo. Head to Playa Blanca. That's most likely where I'll end up, assuming I make it out of Maine without dying of dysentery or getting shot by the cops.

If I don't make it, tell the world my story. Tell them I studied geology, the study of pressure and time. But I wish I'd studied epidemiology, the study of how not to get your shit wrecked by microscopic organisms hell bent on your destruction.

If I do make it out of here, and you wish to join me, bring antibiotics and antivirals. Tons of them. As many as you can get your hands on. You know what Mexicans say about the Pacific? They say it has no memory. And you know what Mexicans say about the Mexican healthcare system? They say, La medicina no es muy buena.

Lastly, bring a set of left-handed tools. My right arm is looking really, really, bad. Hope is a good thing, sure. But you know what's an even better thing? Science. That's the only thing standing between us and virulent plagues that make you hallucinate that Raquel Welch is wrapping her flagella around you during steamy, tantric germ sex.

So, yeah, when you come to Mexico, bring lots of medication. I have a feeling the water down there is going to fuck us up all over again.

Meanwhile, at a Gin Joint in the Maghreb...

— It's a load of bullshit is what it is. A heaping load of bullshit.

When you work with a man for that many years, you'd think he'd show you a bit of loyalty, you know?

Don't get me wrong, he's a white fella who runs a night-club in the forties, I wasn't exactly expecting Abe Lincoln levels of integrity. But still, you figure, we stuck together in Paris, we stuck together here, he's not gonna skip town without making sure I at least got some kind of steady gig lined up. But, oh well, guess old Sam's gonna have to figure shit out on his own again. Ain't the first time, won't be the last.

And look, I don't fault the man. Ilsa was his girl. I get it. I was there in the room with the two of them back in Mont-martre. "We'll always have Paris" and "Who's looking at who, kid," and all that other lovey-dovey crap. They said all that stuff right in front of me. They're always whispering sweet nothings like that to each other right in front of me like I'm not even there. It's weird.

So, yeah, when she showed up with Laszlo, I didn't buy Rick's cold shoulder routine for a second. "Of all the gin joints in all the towns in all the world, she walks into mine." Gimme a break. You run the most popular night-club in the town that's the number-one destination for resistance fighters fleeing the Nazis and trying to get their transit papers so they can get to the United States. And you're telling me you don't think she's going to pass through town at some point? You could've gone to Swit-zerland and waited it out, but instead you bought the *one* gin joint in the *one* town in all the world she'd be *most* likely to walk into. Save me the histrionics, pal.

The way I see it, Rick knew deep down this would happen eventually. And putting her on that plane to Portugal with Laszlo after that whole "hill of beans" speech? That's classic Rick. Always finding a way to make himself the hero of his own story.

You know what's not classic Rick, though? Leaving his loyal jazz pianist friend stranded in a foreign country where he can't get a decent job because all the clubs are run by career criminals. I mean, the man spends years keeping his hands clean, staying out of the smuggling game, never once making any deals with scumbags like Signor Ferrari. Then, all of a sudden, he turns around and sells his club to that low-life? Like that's gonna wrap up all his business affairs in a neat little bow? Like that's gonna make sure his buddy Sam is looked after? Gimme a break. Ferrari had repeatedly offered to pay me two, even three times what Rick was paying me, and I turned him down every single time. And Rick thinks I'm suddenly gonna take a job there and everything's gonna be fine?

I knew as soon as I walked into Ferrari's joint exactly what was going to go down. And sure enough, what's the first thing that greaseball does on my first day on the job? He tries to rope me into some little fake passport con he's got going. Nice try. I'm a Black man who lived through Prohibition *and* the Depression. I know better than to get involved in any racket with a shady Italian.

Because you know what's gonna happen the minute Ferrari gets raided by the Vichy police? He's gonna slip them a bribe, point the finger at me, and say "That's him right over there, officers," and then guess who spends the rest of the war rotting in a Moroccan prison? That's right, yours truly. Well, I don't think so. I've been around the block too many times to fall for that shit.

But now I'm stuck in this dusty desert town with no job and not enough dough to get back to the States even if I wanted to go. Which I don't, 'cause the States ain't exactly the best place to be right now for folks like me, on account of all the segregation and the lynching and the general racism, which was the whole reason I moved to France in the first place.

Meanwhile, he's on his way to Brazzaville, smoking cigars and drinking whiskey with his new French pal. "This is

the beginning of a beautiful friendship?" What about the
beautiful friendship you already had with your old buddy
Sam? The one who was there to console you after Ilsa left?
The one who kept an eye on the club all those times you
were on the sauce? The one who scrubbed the toilet
afterwards each time you knocked back a few too many
French 75s to help you "forget?" I guess the problems of
one Black man in Nazi-occupied French Morocco don't
amount to a hill of beans in this crazy world either, as far
as you're concerned.

And you know what the worst part about looking after
Rick all those years was? Having to play that damn song.
It was always, "Play it again, Sam." Never, "Surprise me,
Sam." Or, "Shake things up a little, Sam." Or, "Why don't
you play one of those original compositions you've been
working so hard on, Sam?" Would it kill Rick to add a little
variety? The man's got a piano-playing best friend who
gives Art Tatum a run for his money and he's got him
playing one doggone song over and over again like one of
those damn mechanical player pianos.

But I still did it. I played that song so many times I can
play it backwards, with my eyes closed, and stoned out
of my mind. And what do I get in return? Stranded in
North Africa with a couple "IOUs" and a hostile Vichy
patrol squad that's bound to come around asking
questions.

That's why my advice to you is to get out of this god-
forsaken snake den the minute you can. Because if you

don't, you'll regret it. Maybe not today. Maybe not tomorrow. But soon and for the rest of your life. That's what I
think.

— Okay, but I asked you what you want to *drink*?

— Oh, just the usual.

Recently Declassified COINTELPRO File on Mr. Forrest Gump

The following documents have been declassified after a Freedom of Information Act filing by the American Civil Liberties Union.

––––––––

October 23, 1967

TO: Mr. J. Edgar Hoover, Director, FBI
FROM: Mr. W. C. Sullivan, Lead Investigator, COINTELPRO
COUNTERINTELLIGENCE PROGRAM
SECURITY MATTER — NEW LEFT

Director Hoover,

I am writing to call your attention to a previously unknown activist by the name of Forrest Gump, believed to be a member of the National Mobilization Committee to End the War in Vietnam, who was first identified during yesterday's March on the Pentagon.

Gump addressed the crowd gathered on the steps of the Lincoln Memorial alongside prominent activist Abbie Hoffman and spoke about his service in the Vietnam War. Broadcast of the speech was interrupted by a member of the 82nd Airborne Division deployed to disrupt the protest, but FBI agents planted within the crowd report that Gump gave a blistering account of torrential rainfall, repeated enemy bombardment, and the tragic death of a G.I. named "Bubba" who was, in Private Gump's words, his "best good friend."

———

October 24, 1967

TO: Mr. W. C. Sullivan, Lead Investigator, COINTELPRO
FROM: Mr. J. Edgar Hoover, Director, FBI
COUNTERINTELLIGENCE PROGRAM
SECURITY MATTER — NEW LEFT

Agent Sullivan,

Get me everything you can find on Gump, put a tail on him, and get me his commanding officer on the phone, ASAP.

———

October 27, 1967

TO: Mr. J. Edgar Hoover, Director, FBI

FROM: Mr. W. C. Sullivan, Lead Investigator, COINTELPRO

COUNTERINTELLIGENCE PROGRAM

SECURITY MATTER — NEW LEFT

Director Hoover,

    I have pulled additional background on
Private Gump, as requested. Ninth Infantry Division.
Served one six-month deployment. Commanding officer,
Lieutenant Dan Taylor. Identity of the best friend
named during the March on the Pentagon speech has
been confirmed: Benjamin Buford "Bubba" Blue. DOB:
March 2nd 1943. Was K.I.A. during an ambush near
the Mekong Delta.

    But here's where it gets interesting. Gump
received a Medal of Honor for saving three men—
P.F.C. Dallas from Phoenix, P.F.C. Cleveland from
Detroit, P.F.C. Tex (birthplace unknown)—as well as
his commanding officer during the ambush. Secret
Service has confirmed that Gump was awarded the
Medal of Honor at the White House on October 21.
During the ceremony he proceeded to expose his
buttocks to President Johnson, before leaving the
White House and joining the protest approximately
twenty-five minutes later.

    Commanding officer, Lt. Dan Taylor, has been
contacted, but refuses to cooperate with our

investigation, saying, "You goddamn FBI sons of bitches can all go straight the fuck to hell."

———————

October 30, 1967

TO: Mr. W. C. Sullivan, Lead Investigator, COINTELPRO
FROM: Mr. J. Edgar Hoover, Director, FBI
COUNTERINTELLIGENCE PROGRAM
SECURITY MATTER — NEW LEFT

Agent Sullivan,

Are you telling me we let a goddamn hippie get close enough to moon the President of the United States? This suggests some sort of deep cover program within the anti-war movement. We need more eyes on Gump. We cannot let this man near the President again. Once was one time too many.

———————

November 1, 1967

TO: Mr. J. Edgar Hoover, Director, FBI
FROM: Mr. W. C. Sullivan, Lead Investigator, COINTELPRO
COUNTERINTELLIGENCE PROGRAM
SECURITY MATTER — NEW LEFT

Director Hoover,

You are not going to believe this, but Gump has met the sitting president not once, but twice. White House visitor logs from '62 show a Forrest Gump meeting President Kennedy during a visit of the 1962 NCAA Football All-American team. We found the AP press release confirming a Forrest Gump on the '62 All-American team. Kick return specialist.

It gets worse, though. We talked to a few of the other players, and one of them said that, when Gump went to shake hands with the President, Jack asked, "How do you feel?" and Gump said, "I have to pee." We have reason to believe it might be some sort of sick joke about Kennedy's Addison's Disease. No clue how Gump got his hands on that classified intel.

We have eyes and ears on Gump. If he so much as sneezes, we'll know about it.

––––––––

November 9, 1967

TO: Mr. W. C. Sullivan, Lead Investigator, COINTELPRO
FROM: Mr. J. Edgar Hoover, Director, FBI
COUNTERINTELLIGENCE PROGRAM
SECURITY MATTER — NEW LEFT

Agent Sullivan,

    What kind of sick son of a bitch steals
classified intel on the president just to taunt
him with it? This means Gump's been in deep
cover since at least '61. He got within striking
distance of two U.S. Presidents and it took us
six years just to get a whiff of him? I mean
there's no telling where else this guy's got his
tentacles buried. What's next? He's friends with
Elvis and hangs out with the Black Panthers? I'm
almost afraid to ask, but is there anything on
Gump in the Warren Report?

——————

November 14, 1967

TO: Mr. J. Edgar Hoover, Director, FBI
FROM: Mr. W. C. Sullivan, Lead Investigator, COINTELPRO
COUNTERINTELLIGENCE PROGRAM
SECURITY MATTER — NEW LEFT

Director Hoover,

    No, he's squeaky clean as far as the Warren
Report goes. No ties to ▇▇▇▇ over at Central
Intelligence who ordered ▇▇▇▇▇▇▇▇▇▇▇▇
to ▇▇▇▇▇▇▇▇▇▇▇▇ Jimmy Hoffa ▇▇▇▇▇▇

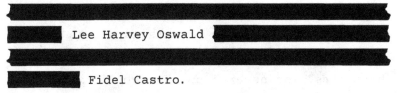

Lee Harvey Oswald

Fidel Castro.

But we did some digging into his college years and found a complaint filed to Campus Housing over at another school by the roommate of Jenny Curran, alleging that Curran brought Gump into her room after hours and engaged in inappropriate behavior with him (light fondling, no intercourse). We checked, and Curran has been on our radar for some time for her involvement in the anti-war movement.

Birth certificates show they're both from Greenbow, Alabama, so the two are likely childhood friends. We think she's the one who recruited him to these New Left social movements going back to their early college years. No indication of a romantic relationship at this time (she is involved with some other hippie we've been monitoring) but Gump and Curran do seem to have sort of an on-again, off-again, will-they-or-won't-they thing going on.

Either way, their relationship points to Gump being embedded in anti-government organizations for years now. One thing's for sure—this goes way deeper than we previously thought.

We'll keep digging up dirt on Gump. In the meantime, here's something to chew on. We bugged

Gump's room and he said the damndest thing the
other day. He's talking to someone and he goes,
"My momma always says life is like a box of
chocolates. You never know what you're gonna
get." We couldn't tell who he was talking to,
but what do you make of it? Is it some sort of
elaborate cipher? A passphrase, maybe? I've got
a team of cryptographers trying to crack it,
but they haven't come up with anything yet
beyond it being a folksy aphorism about the
uncertainty inherent in the human experience.
Thoughts?

———

November 16, 1967

TO: Mr. W. C. Sullivan, Lead Investigator, COINTELPRO
FROM: Mr. J. Edgar Hoover, Director, FBI
COUNTERINTELLIGENCE PROGRAM
SECURITY MATTER — NEW LEFT

LIFE IS LIKE A BOX OF CHOCOLATES?!?!? What
the hell does that mean? Shit. This is really bad.
You realize what this means? He's onto us,
Sullivan. He and his people know we've got him
bugged, and they've developed some sort of Enigma-
type machine that cranks out homespun adages we
can't crack!

I'm gobsmacked. These lazy, dope-smoking hippies somehow managed to embed a deep cover agent onto the University of Alabama football team in 1961 just to see whether they could get him close to the President. Then sent that same agent on a deployment to the Vietnam War to earn a Medal of Honor just to make a mockery of the award. I mean, talk about playing the long game.

This movement is far more organized and sophisticated than we ever could have imagined.

I've seen enough. I'm calling together a full team devoted to Gump. I want eyes on everyone he's meeting and everyone he's ever had ties to. We need a task force dedicated to delegitimizing Gump, disrupting his activist efforts, and, if necessary, taking him out of the equation entirely. Have your team assembled by the end of the month.

And, this goes without saying, but do not inform the President. This is so goddamn embarrassing as it is, and I don't want him finding out that we let some rogue hippie flash him the full moon as part of some twisted anti-government demonstration.

Operation Box of Chocolates is now in full swing.

———

November 16, 1967

TO: Mr. C. A. Tolson, Associate Director, FBI
FROM: Mr. J. Edgar Hoover, Director, FBI
COUNTERINTELLIGENCE PROGRAM
SECURITY MATTER — NEW LEFT

Clyde,

    I'm sorry, but we're going to have to cancel
our trip to Del Mar this year. I was so looking
forward to our private suite at the racetrack, but
Operation Box of Chocolates is going to require
all hands on deck. Let's discuss our game plan
tonight over dinner.

November 16, 1967

TO: Mr. J. Edgar Hoover, Director, FBI
FROM: Mr. C. A. Tolson, Associate Director, FBI
COUNTERINTELLIGENCE PROGRAM
SECURITY MATTER — NEW LEFT

J.,

    Ugh, fine. But you owe me.

November 20, 1967

TO: Mr. J. Edgar Hoover, Director, FBI

FROM: Mr. W. C. Sullivan, Lead Investigator, COINTELPRO

COUNTERINTELLIGENCE PROGRAM

SECURITY MATTER — NEW LEFT

Director Hoover,

We've received intel that Gump met with the
Black Panthers while he was in Washington. Our guy
on the inside confirmed that a man matching Gump's
exact description (tall, quiet, deceptively simple-
minded, loves to run) was involved in an
altercation with an activist during a clandestine
Panther meeting shortly after the March on the
Pentagon.

November 21, 1967

TO: Mr. W. C. Sullivan, Lead Investigator, COINTELPRO

FROM: Mr. J. Edgar Hoover, Director, FBI

COUNTERINTELLIGENCE PROGRAM

SECURITY MATTER — NEW LEFT

Agent Sullivan,

So he's got ties to the Panthers after all. I

knew it. This guy's everywhere. Every single social movement, he's a part of it. Every historical moment, he's there. I mean, how in the hell can one person manage to get himself in all of these places? This just reinforces why we need a task force to stop this guy, whatever he's planning. Do we know anything about his motivations yet? What he's after? Is he strictly anti-war or are we talking full government overthrow, Kremlin ties, that sort of thing? We've known about this guy for a month. How do we not have more intel on him?

Glad to hear there's been infighting, though. At least something we're doing is working.

————————

November 27, 1967

TO: Mr. J. Edgar Hoover, Director, FBI
FROM: Mr. W. C. Sullivan, Lead Investigator, COINTELPRO
COUNTERINTELLIGENCE PROGRAM
SECURITY MATTER — NEW LEFT

Director Hoover,

We still can't crack Gump's coded messages. We've had him bugged for five weeks and he's given us zilch. He keeps talking about how he "promised Bubba" he'd "buy a shrimp boat" to "shrimp the

Gulf." No idea what any of that means. Our best guess is that "shrimp the Gulf" is code for some sort of retaliation against the government over the war to avenge his friend's death. But that's as far as we've gotten.

We've picked up a couple more of those "sayings" from his "mama," like "you can tell a lot about a person by their shoes" and "stupid is as stupid does," but the team's gotten nowhere trying to decipher them. We don't know if "mama" is an alias, or a codename for another deep cover agent. But every trail we follow goes nowhere. Not sure how, but Gump always seems to be a step ahead of us. I've never encountered anyone with this level of genius. Gump is truly in a league of his own.

———

November 30, 1967

TO: Mr. W. C. Sullivan, Lead Investigator, COINTELPRO
FROM: Mr. J. Edgar Hoover, Director, FBI
COUNTERINTELLIGENCE PROGRAM
SECURITY MATTER — NEW LEFT

Agent Sullivan,

SHRIMP THE GULF?!?! That sick motherfucker. Whatever he's got planned, we can't let it happen.

There's gotta be a way in on this guy. What's his vice? Women? All the powerful guys love cheating on their wives with tons of women. If we catch Gump on tape, we could always suicide letter him. Didn't work with King, but it's worth a shot. Then again, Gump's an unmarried twenty-three-year-old man living with his mother, so maybe women aren't the angle we ought to be gunning for.

Is he a booze hound? The way he talks, you'd swear he was drinking himself under the table. Then again, he seems too damn sharp to be an alky, or a dope fiend for that matter. Still, see what you can find.

———

March 26, 1968

TO: Mr. J. Edgar Hoover, Director, FBI
FROM: Mr. W. C. Sullivan, Lead Investigator, COINTELPRO
COUNTERINTELLIGENCE PROGRAM
SECURITY MATTER — NEW LEFT

Director Hoover,

We've been tailing Gump for months and still don't have anything on him. Not a single woman, no booze, no smack, no grass, nothing. The occasional beer, that's it. I've never met a hippie so goddamn clean in all my years here. The only thing he seems to be "addicted" to is ping-pong. He's actually quite good at it. Weirdly good.

I'm starting to wonder if he's even our guy. What if he's just a simpleton from Alabama who happened to be at the right place at the right time during several decisive moments of American history? I know it sounds nuts, but our team has spent six months trying to break the Box of Chocolates Cipher and they still don't have a single lead.

On a related note, King is going to be in Memphis in a couple days and ████████████ civil rights ██████████████████ socialism ████████ ████████████████████████ income inequality ██████████████████████ we have everything in place.

———

April 8, 1968

TO: Mr. W. C. Sullivan, Lead Investigator, COINTELPRO
FROM: Mr. J. Edgar Hoover, Director, FBI
COUNTERINTELLIGENCE PROGRAM
SECURITY MATTER — NEW LEFT

Agent Sullivan,

Have you lost your goddamn mind? A simpleton from Alabama? Who has shaken hands with two presidents of the United States and spoken on the steps of the Lincoln Memorial? Use your head. The fact that he's squeaky clean only increases my suspicions. To be so resolute of purpose that he refuses to give in to the baser instincts even once suggests that we're dealing with some kind of hyper-idealistic megalomaniac. Maybe he's even got the Soviets pumping him full of some brand-new pharmaceutical that squelches the id by sending the superego into overdrive. We had our guys working on that, but all "LSD" did was make people see crazy patterns on the wall and draw a bunch of weird shit.

Explore the ping-pong angle. Gump doesn't do anything by "accident" or "strange historical coincidence." If he's playing ping-pong, there's got to be a reason.

Now that King is out of the way, we need to turn our full attention to Gump. He is enemy of the people #1 as far as I'm concerned. How can we neutralize him? Have you considered ██████████

███████████████████████████████████
███████████████████████████████████
███████████████████████████████████
███████████████████████████████████

████████████████ Malcolm X? ██████████
███████████████████████████████████

██████ Che Guevara?

April 9, 1968

TO: Mr. J. Edgar Hoover, Director, FBI
FROM: Mr. W. C. Sullivan, Lead Investigator, COINTELPRO
COUNTERINTELLIGENCE PROGRAM
SECURITY MATTER — NEW LEFT

Director Hoover,

You're absolutely right. I don't know what I
was thinking. I will explore our options re:
neutralizing Gump. Our usual technique of ███████
█████████████████████ too difficult ███████████
███
███████████████████████ plant some drugs
██████████ pin the blame on ██████████████████

———————

May 21, 1968

TO: Mr. W. C. Sullivan, Lead Investigator, COINTELPRO
FROM: Mr. J. Edgar Hoover, Director, FBI
COUNTERINTELLIGENCE PROGRAM
SECURITY MATTER — NEW LEFT

Agent Sullivan,

██
██████████████████████████ shrimp ███████████

██
████ DEFCON 3 ████████████████████████████████████
██
███████████████ Puerto Ricans ███████████████████
██
██

Does that all make sense?

———————

May 22, 1968

TO: Mr. J. Edgar Hoover, Director, FBI
FROM: Mr. W. C. Sullivan, Lead Investigator, COINTELPRO
COUNTERINTELLIGENCE PROGRAM
SECURITY MATTER — NEW LEFT

Director Hoover,

    Makes perfect sense to me.

———————

May 31, 1968

TO: Mr. W. C. Sullivan, Lead Investigator, COINTELPRO
FROM: Mr. J. Edgar Hoover, Director, FBI
COUNTERINTELLIGENCE PROGRAM
SECURITY MATTER — NEW LEFT

Agent Sullivan,

    Walk me through the plan again.

June 3, 1968

TO: Mr. J. Edgar Hoover, Director, FBI
FROM: Mr. W. C. Sullivan, Lead Investigator, COINTELPRO
COUNTERINTELLIGENCE PROGRAM
SECURITY MATTER — NEW LEFT

Director Hoover,

June 7, 1968

TO: Mr. W. C. Sullivan, Lead Investigator, COINTELPRO
FROM: Mr. J. Edgar Hoover, Director, FBI
COUNTERINTELLIGENCE PROGRAM
SECURITY MATTER — NEW LEFT

Agent Sullivan,

How the hell did Sirhan get Forrest Gump and
Bobby Kennedy mixed up?
Keep eyes on Gump, but stand down on
neutralization efforts until further notice. LBJ's
gonna be on my ass about this and we'd better lie
low.

———————

November 12, 1968

TO: Mr. W. C. Sullivan, Lead Investigator, COINTELPRO
FROM: Mr. J. Edgar Hoover, Director, FBI
COUNTERINTELLIGENCE PROGRAM
SECURITY MATTER — NEW LEFT

Agent Sullivan,

I've been thinking about that Box of Chocolates
Cipher again. Could it be some sort of anagram? Does

the phrase "tobacco foxholes" mean anything to you? Some sort of G.I. slang, maybe? Anyway, just something to think about.

———

January 21, 1969

TO: Mr. W. C. Sullivan, Lead Investigator, COINTELPRO
FROM: Mr. J. Edgar Hoover, Director, FBI
COUNTERINTELLIGENCE PROGRAM
SECURITY MATTER — NEW LEFT

Agent Sullivan,

Good news. President Nixon has been briefed on Operation Box of Chocolates and we are clear to resume (non-lethal) disruption tactics. Any movement on Gump?

———

January 22, 1969

TO: Mr. J. Edgar Hoover, Director, FBI
FROM: Mr. W. C. Sullivan, Lead Investigator, COINTELPRO
COUNTERINTELLIGENCE PROGRAM
SECURITY MATTER — NEW LEFT

Director Hoover,

Got it. There's not much to report. He's
just been playing ping-pong. A lot of ping-pong.
We've been watching our surveillance tapes on
him and, frankly, it's mesmerizing. No word yet
on what his motivation is, but he's really good.
He might be one of the best players in the
country.

————————

January 23, 1969

TO: Mr. W. C. Sullivan, Lead Investigator, COINTELPRO
FROM: Mr. J. Edgar Hoover, Director, FBI
COUNTERINTELLIGENCE PROGRAM
SECURITY MATTER — NEW LEFT

Agent Sullivan,

Okay, well don't take your eye off the ball
(no pun intended). I know he's up to something.
Nobody in their right mind would ever play that
much ping-pong just for the hell of it.

————————

July 17, 1969

TO: Mr. W. C. Sullivan, Lead Investigator, COINTELPRO
FROM: Mr. J. Edgar Hoover, Director, FBI
COUNTERINTELLIGENCE PROGRAM
SECURITY MATTER — NEW LEFT

Agent Sullivan,

Just had an idea. What do you think about

suicide?

———

July 18, 1969

TO: Mr. J. Edgar Hoover, Director, FBI
FROM: Mr. W. C. Sullivan, Lead Investigator, COINTELPRO
COUNTERINTELLIGENCE PROGRAM
SECURITY MATTER — NEW LEFT

Director Hoover,

    I phoned their office, but they're using the
studio to stage something else this weekend.

——————

                                    December 5, 1969

TO: Mr. J. Edgar Hoover, Director, FBI
FROM: Mr. W. C. Sullivan, Lead Investigator, COINTELPRO
COUNTERINTELLIGENCE PROGRAM
SECURITY MATTER — NEW LEFT

Director Hoover,

    We searched Fred Hampton's apartment after
the raid. Nothing linking him to Gump. In fact,
we haven't heard or seen a single thing tying
Gump to the Panthers other than that one meeting
he attended. All we found in the apartment was a
couple moving boxes full of breakfast cereal,
oatmeal, and fruit labeled "Free Breakfast For
The Children."
    I'm kind of starting to wonder if maybe we
didn't have the full story there?
    Are we 100 percent sure Gump is who we think
he is? Because we keep neutralizing his associates
and not finding what we're looking for.

December 8, 1969

TO: Mr. W. C. Sullivan, Lead Investigator, COINTELPRO
FROM: Mr. J. Edgar Hoover, Director, FBI
COUNTERINTELLIGENCE PROGRAM
SECURITY MATTER — NEW LEFT

Agent Sullivan,

Don't be thick. Did you really expect a mastermind like Forrest Gump to leave obvious tracks? Coming up short on evidence and concluding that he's just a bumpkin from a Podunk town in Alabama—who unwittingly stumbled his way through every major watershed moment in mid-to-late-twentieth-century America—is exactly what he wants you to believe.

Think, Sullivan! THINK!

What do we know about this Jenny broad? Is there anything on her we can use to nail Gump? He's said himself they're like "peas and carrots." There's gonna be a way to use her to get to him.

December 10, 1969

TO: Mr. J. Edgar Hoover, Director, FBI
FROM: Mr. W. C. Sullivan, Lead Investigator, COINTELPRO
COUNTERINTELLIGENCE PROGRAM
SECURITY MATTER — NEW LEFT

Director Hoover,

   Our intel suggests Forrest and Jenny haven't
been in contact since the March on the Pentagon.
For two people that are, by his admission, like
"peas and carrots," she really doesn't seem that
interested in keeping in touch with him. I almost
feel bad for the guy?
   She is in San Francisco and we believe she
no longer poses a threat to national security. Our
guys on the inside of the anti-war movement have
pretty much all of them hooked on heroin. It's
crazy how effective heroin is at destroying social
movements. You know that phrase "like a moth to a
flame?" They should say "like a hippie to heroin"
instead. They can't get enough of the stuff. And
just wait until we get Operation C.R.A.C.K. going.
   Once the drugs become pervasive, we're
thinking that'll give us an excuse to declare a
"War On The Drugs" as a way to further disrupt
these movements. How does that sound?

———————

December 11, 1969

TO: Mr. W. C. Sullivan, Lead Investigator, COINTELPRO
FROM: Mr. J. Edgar Hoover, Director, FBI
COUNTERINTELLIGENCE PROGRAM
SECURITY MATTER — NEW LEFT

Agent Sullivan,

    Drop the "The." It's cleaner.

———————

May 5, 1970

TO: Mr. J. Edgar Hoover, Director, FBI
FROM: Mr. W. C. Sullivan, Lead Investigator, COINTELPRO
COUNTERINTELLIGENCE PROGRAM
SECURITY MATTER — NEW LEFT

Director Hoover,

██████████████████████████████████████

███

██

███

██

██████   Kent State ████████████████████████

██

███████████

May 6, 1970

TO: Mr. W. C. Sullivan, Lead Investigator, COINTELPRO
FROM: Mr. J. Edgar Hoover, Director, FBI
COUNTERINTELLIGENCE PROGRAM
SECURITY MATTER — NEW LEFT

Agent Sullivan,

If Gump wasn't even there, then what the hell
was the point?

April 6, 1971

TO: Mr. J. Edgar Hoover, Director, FBI
FROM: Mr. W. C. Sullivan, Lead Investigator, COINTELPRO
COUNTERINTELLIGENCE PROGRAM
SECURITY MATTER — NEW LEFT

Director Hoover,

You are not going to believe this, but Forrest
Gump is currently in Nagoya, Japan competing in the
World Table Tennis Championships.

And guess which country invited the team to
visit? China.

April 7, 1971

TO: Mr. W. C. Sullivan, Lead Investigator, COINTELPRO
FROM: Mr. J. Edgar Hoover, Director, FBI
COUNTERINTELLIGENCE PROGRAM
SECURITY MATTER — NEW LEFT

I KNEW IT! I goddamn knew it! That commie
son of a bitch must've been planning this for
years. Getting good at ping-pong just to get an
audience with Chairman Mao himself. You see,
Sullivan? Just when you think he's got no ulterior
motives, just when you think he's some auspicious
small-town redneck, that's when he pulls a fast
one on you.

Have the codebreaking team analyze "Box of
Chocolates" for any connections to ping-pong and
China. Does chocolate originate in China? It seems
like those people invented everything.

And send agents to accompany the team. And
don't let Gump out of your sight while he's in
China. There's no telling what that wily son of a
gun will do.

April 7, 1971

TO: Mr. J. Edgar Hoover, Director, FBI
FROM: Mr. C. A. Tolson, Associate Director, FBI
COUNTERINTELLIGENCE PROGRAM
SECURITY MATTER — NEW LEFT

J.,

    You're not taking me to the Derby this year?
Are you fucking kidding me?

                    ————————

April 15, 1971

TO: Mr. J. Edgar Hoover, Director, FBI
FROM: Mr. W. C. Sullivan, Lead Investigator, COINTELPRO
COUNTERINTELLIGENCE PROGRAM
SECURITY MATTER — NEW LEFT

Director Hoover,

    We kept an eye on Gump during the entire
trip. He did nothing but eat, sleep, play ping-
pong, and make pleasant small talk with
everyone he encountered. If he had tried to
sneak out of his hotel, or tried to slip someone
a coded message, we would've seen it. It's

possible he was aware he was being monitored and aborted his mission. We'll continue keeping tabs on him.

———

April 16, 1971

TO: Mr. W. C. Sullivan, Lead Investigator, COINTELPRO
FROM: Mr. J. Edgar Hoover, Director, FBI
COUNTERINTELLIGENCE PROGRAM
SECURITY MATTER — NEW LEFT

Agent Sullivan,

Good. Very good. If he was unable to carry out his mission that means we're doing something right. But it could be that this was just a recon mission, just getting the lay of the land in Beijing. We're not out of the woods yet.

I phoned his commanding officer in the Army Special Services, and you know what that goddamn moron said to me? He said he had no reason to believe Gump was anything other than a "war hero, an upstanding gentleman, and a damn fine ping-pong player." So I said, "Well, no shit, that's what you think, you ignorant dumbass. Because you haven't been monitoring this man's whereabouts for the past four years." Then when I told him to

discharge Gump because he's a threat to national
security, this dunce has the gall to laugh in my
face and tell me I must be out of my damn mind.

I will get Gump discharged if it's the last
thing I do. Even if I have to phone Dickie myself.

————

June 15, 1971

TO: Mr. W. C. Sullivan, Lead Investigator, COINTELPRO
FROM: Mr. J. Edgar Hoover, Director, FBI
COUNTERINTELLIGENCE PROGRAM
SECURITY MATTER — NEW LEFT

That yellow-bellied communist traitor is on
TV gallivanting with Dick Cavett and that godless
druggie John Lennon! I've never seen anything so
despicable in my life! Talking about how people
in China never go to church. No shit, you damn
pinko bastard! I swear, that stupid drawl of his
and that phony clean-cut, upstanding act he's got
going on. I'd like to punch that man square in
the jaw. Gump better pray he and I never cross
paths.

Tell me he isn't up to something!

————

June 16, 1971

TO: Mr. J. Edgar Hoover, Director, FBI

FROM: Mr. W. C. Sullivan, Lead Investigator, COINTELPRO

COUNTERINTELLIGENCE PROGRAM

SECURITY MATTER — NEW LEFT

Director Hoover,

    I keep running everything we know about
Gump through my mind, and I hate to say it, but I
think we might've gotten it wrong.

    It's been four years and we still haven't
come up with anything concrete to nail Gump on.
Coincidentally appearing at multiple pivotal
moments in the tumultuous decade of the 1960s is
not a crime. At least not as far as I'm aware?
What if we've been blinded by groupthink
mentality and our own hubris? What if Gump is
just some guy?

———

June 18, 1971

TO: Mr. W. C. Sullivan, Lead Investigator, COINTELPRO

FROM: Mr. J. Edgar Hoover, Director, FBI

COUNTERINTELLIGENCE PROGRAM

SECURITY MATTER — NEW LEFT

Agent Sullivan,

    You stupid idiot. How many times have we
been through this? Once is a coincidence, twice
is an alarming trend, three times is too
suspicious to ignore. And Gump? There's so many
coincidences I've lost count. He's trouble, and I
want him discharged from the Army and then I
want him dead in a ditch. It's as simple as
that.

    By the way, Dick liked your War on Drugs
idea so much he's expanding it to every low-income
neighborhood in the entire country. You should be
very proud.

                        ————————

                                September 30, 1971

TO: Mr. J. Edgar Hoover, Director, FBI
FROM: Mr. W. C. Sullivan, Lead Investigator, COINTELPRO
COUNTERINTELLIGENCE PROGRAM
SECURITY MATTER — NEW LEFT

Director Hoover,

    I'm not normally one to disagree with you.
Lord knows I've had my suspicions about Gump too
over the years, but I no longer think we can
justify the enormous resources we've devoted to

monitor, disrupt, and delegitimize Gump just to come up empty-handed every time.

The KKK just blew up a bunch of school buses outside Detroit to protest school integration. That's Detroit, Michigan. MICHIGAN. That's not even one of the super racist states, just one of the regular racist states, like California or Massachusetts. We've been so focused on Gump we've completely dropped the ball on white supremacy. And you fired practically the entire corporate fraud division so you could hire a team of experts to solve the "Shrimp the Gulf" riddle. Meanwhile, you've only got two agents on the Zodiac Cipher because it's "boring by comparison." What if Gump just wants to go into the shrimping business like he promised his friend Bubba he would?

Don't mistake my disagreement for disloyalty. I was totally onboard when we ███████████

████████████████████████████████████

████████████████████ redlining ███████

████████████████████████████████████

████████████████████████████████████

████████ Area 51 ████████████████████

████████████████████████████████████

████████████████████████████████████

████████ fluoride ████████████████████

██████████

But I urge you to rethink this obsession with Forrest Gump.

———

September 30, 1971

TO: Mr. W. C. Sullivan, Lead Investigator, COINTELPRO
FROM: Mr. J. Edgar Hoover, Director, FBI
COUNTERINTELLIGENCE PROGRAM
SECURITY MATTER — NEW LEFT

Agent Sullivan,

If you've been so brainwashed by Gump's obvious facade of innocence that you're unwilling to do what needs to be done, then I'll find someone who will.

Don't bother showing up to work tomorrow.

———

October 1, 1971

TO: All Bureau Offices
FROM: Mr. J. Edgar Hoover, Director, FBI
COUNTERINTELLIGENCE PROGRAM
SECURITY MATTER — NEW LEFT

Associate Director William Sullivan has been terminated as of yesterday afternoon. There is evidence to suggest he may be compromised. All agents are ordered to cease official communication

as well as personal communication with Agent
Sullivan until further notice.

October 1, 1971

TO: Richard M. Nixon, President of the United States
FROM: Mr. J. Edgar Hoover, Director, FBI
COUNTERINTELLIGENCE PROGRAM
SECURITY MATTER — NEW LEFT

Mr. President,

I am writing to inform you that I have
terminated Bureau Associate Director William
Sullivan effective yesterday. He will be replaced
by agent Mark Felt. Mr. Felt is a man of tremendous
character who I can say with certainty is a man
you and I can both trust.

October 1, 1971

TO: Mr. J. Edgar Hoover, Director, FBI
FROM: Mr. W. M. Felt, Lead Investigator, COINTELPRO
COUNTERINTELLIGENCE PROGRAM
SECURITY MATTER — NEW LEFT

Director Hoover,

    Thank you for putting your trust in me. I
hope I'll make the Bureau proud.

    I have been briefed on Private Gump and, may
I just say, I completely agree with you. He is the
number-one threat to national security and must
be neutralized. Agent Sullivan's inability to
recognize that only furthers my suspicions.

    On a related note, is there any connection
between Gump and the whispers I've been hearing
about an intelligence operation against the
Democratic National Committee? Just curious!

———

                                  October 2, 1971

TO: Mr. W. M. Felt, Lead Investigator, COINTELPRO
FROM: Mr. J. Edgar Hoover, Director, FBI
COUNTERINTELLIGENCE PROGRAM
SECURITY MATTER — NEW LEFT

Agent Felt,

    No connection between the DNC and Gump that
I'm aware of. But I'll have an agent fax you all
the dirt we've gathered so far on the DNC if you
think there might be a connection. Gump has his

commie tentacles everywhere, so I wouldn't be surprised if we end up finding ties.

You have my authorization to initiate any operations you see fit to take Gump out of the equation. He's been a thumb in my ass for the past four years and I think you might be the man to do what Sullivan didn't have the courage to. Go get that son of a bitch!

———

January 2, 1972

TO: Mr. J. Edgar Hoover, Director, FBI
FROM: Mr. W. M. Felt, Lead Investigator, COINTELPRO
COUNTERINTELLIGENCE PROGRAM
SECURITY MATTER — NEW LEFT

Director Hoover,

We almost had him! After we received intel that Gump would be rendezvousing with former commanding officer Lt. Dan Taylor, we had two agents pose as prostitutes to try to nail the both of them for solicitation. And by God we were this close to putting him away for good. But just when it looked like he was going to give in, Gump shoves her away, gets into a huge argument with Lt. Dan, along with the girls, and the whole thing went tits up (literally, one of the agents is being treated for a minor contusion on her left breast).

But I'm encouraged that we were able to get so close to taking him down. The rekindled friendship between Gump and Lt. Dan is something I believe we can exploit, as Lt. Dan is compromised in more ways than I can count. Although he has thus far refused to be an informant for us (his exact words were "I thought I told you goddamn spooks to fuck right off") I still believe we may be able to turn him.

Lt. Dan is also extremely addicted to drugs and alcohol, so that's another tick in the win column for the FBI!

————

January 3, 1972

TO: Mr. W. M. Felt, Lead Investigator, COINTELPRO
FROM: Mr. J. Edgar Hoover, Director, FBI
COUNTERINTELLIGENCE PROGRAM
SECURITY MATTER — NEW LEFT

Excellent work. I knew I could count on you. Don't take your foot off the gas, we need to take this guy out at any cost.

————

February 14, 1972

TO: Mr. J. Edgar Hoover, Director, FBI
FROM: Mr. W. M. Felt, Lead Investigator, COINTELPRO
COUNTERINTELLIGENCE PROGRAM
SECURITY MATTER — NEW LEFT

Director Hoover,

    I compiled the list of ways to assassinate
Private Gump that you requested and will have it
on your desk tomorrow morning. I don't mean to
toot my own horn, but there's some great stuff in
there. Things I think could be helpful later when
we ▮▮▮▮▮▮▮▮▮▮▮▮▮▮▮▮▮▮▮▮▮▮▮▮▮▮▮▮▮▮▮▮
▮▮▮▮▮▮▮▮▮▮▮▮▮▮▮▮▮▮▮▮▮▮▮▮▮▮▮▮▮▮▮▮▮▮
▮▮▮▮▮▮▮▮▮▮▮▮▮▮▮▮▮▮▮▮▮▮▮▮▮▮▮▮▮▮▮▮▮▮
▮▮▮▮▮▮▮▮▮▮▮▮▮▮▮▮▮▮▮▮
▮▮▮▮▮▮▮▮▮▮▮▮▮▮▮▮▮▮▮▮▮▮▮▮▮▮▮▮▮▮▮▮▮▮
▮▮ Salvador Allende ▮▮▮▮▮▮▮▮▮▮▮▮▮▮
▮▮▮▮▮▮▮▮▮▮▮▮▮▮▮▮▮▮▮▮▮▮▮▮▮▮▮▮▮▮▮▮▮▮
▮▮▮▮▮▮▮▮▮▮▮▮▮▮▮▮ Iran ▮▮▮▮▮▮▮▮▮▮▮▮
▮▮▮▮▮▮▮▮▮▮▮▮▮▮▮▮▮▮▮▮▮▮▮▮▮▮▮▮▮▮▮▮▮▮
▮▮▮▮▮▮▮▮▮▮▮▮▮▮▮▮▮▮▮▮▮▮▮▮▮▮▮▮▮▮▮▮▮▮
▮▮▮▮▮▮▮▮▮▮▮▮▮▮▮▮▮▮▮ Nicaragua ▮▮▮▮
▮▮▮▮▮▮▮▮▮▮▮▮▮▮▮▮▮▮▮▮▮▮▮▮▮▮▮▮▮▮▮▮▮▮
▮▮▮▮▮▮

Now I've got to get going so I can pick up a
box of chocolates for the missus and smooth
things over after all these long nights I've been
spending at the office!

———

February 15, 1972

TO: Mr. W. M. Felt, Lead Investigator, COINTELPRO
FROM: Mr. J. Edgar Hoover, Director, FBI
COUNTERINTELLIGENCE PROGRAM
SECURITY MATTER — NEW LEFT

That's it! Felt, you magnificent bastard! Box
of Chocolates! It all makes sense now! Think about
it. Why has Gump been talking in riddles all
these years? Shrimp the Gulf, Box of Chocolates,
Stupid Is As Stupid Does. They're not just
charming southern colloquialisms. It's all
connected!

President Nixon is visiting China in six
days. Why? To establish a framework for gradually
opening economic ties between two formerly
adversarial nations. Nixon is going to SHRIMP THE
GULF, meaning he's going to shrink (shrimp are
small) the metaphorical diplomatic gulf between
the United States and the People's Republic of
China.

BUT, it's a terrible idea, because opening
up economic ties between China and the United
States is only going to erode domestic
manufacturing over the next several decades and
exponentially grow China's economy while doing
almost nothing to curb the Chinese Communist
Party's authoritarian and militaristic tendencies.
But Nixon is doing it anyway. Why? Because STUPID
IS AS STUPID DOES.

AND, Nixon is going to China to visit the
home country of China's leader, Chairman Mao Tse
Tung, the first time a U.S. President has done so
since the start of the Cold War. And what do you
do when you visit someone's home for the first
time? You bring them a BOX OF CHOCOLATES.

SHRIMP THE GULF. STUPID IS AS STUPID DOES.
BOX OF CHOCOLATES. Gump has been slowly paving the
way for the re-opening of US-CHINA relations.
FIRST by undermining the U.S.'s efforts in the
Vietnam War by sowing anti-war sentiments at
home, causing the United States to pivot in its
diplomatic approach to Asian communist countries.
THEN by fostering a growing national interest in
the sport of table tennis, knowing that it's also
a hugely popular sport in China. Thus paving the
way for an apolitical bonding moment between the
U.S. and China over their mutual affection for
ping-pong. All culminating in President Richard
Nixon visiting a formerly hostile nation with the

hopes of improving relations between the two countries.

But little does he know that the Chinese, with the help of Gump, will likely use the visit to kidnap, coerce, torture, or possibly assassinate Nixon in order to bring the United States under the cruel yoke of communism.

It's all been right there in front of me this whole time, but I just couldn't see it!

I have to warn the President, and inform Gump's commanding officer at Special Services, so we can put a stop to this visit before the People's Liberation Army can use Kung Fu, or water torture, or whatever the hell it is they do over there, to force Nixon into surrender.

February 15, 1972

TO: Mr. W. M. Felt, Lead Investigator, COINTELPRO
FROM: Mr. J. Edgar Hoover, Director, FBI
COUNTERINTELLIGENCE PROGRAM
SECURITY MATTER — NEW LEFT

HE FOILED US AGAIN! HOW? We had Gump under constant surveillance. We knew his plan. The President told me, "J., this is a little extreme even for you, but I'll keep my eyes open." And yet we still didn't catch that sly bugger in the act! The whole visit went off without a hitch! Nixon waved his little peace sign and the press ate that crap up! We're friends with China now! There's a glimmer of hope for an eventual end to the Cold War! What in the Sam Hill?

I want Gump dead! Drag him out into the street and shoot him like a dog if you have to! This ends now!

———

February 16, 1972

TO: Mr. J. Edgar Hoover, Director, FBI
FROM: Mr. W. M. Felt, Lead Investigator, COINTELPRO
COUNTERINTELLIGENCE PROGRAM
SECURITY MATTER — NEW LEFT

Director Hoover,

As much as I'd like to, you know we can't

██

████ celebrity █████████████████████████

I mean, sure ██████████████████████████

███████████████████████████████ Marilyn

Monroe ████████████████ Sam Cooke ██████

██

██

Sharon Tate ████████████████████████████
████████████████████████ but that was the
sixties.

Also, are you feeling okay? Maybe you ought
to take a couple weeks off to do some fishing. I
can handle Gump and the DNC surveillance while
you're out.

————————

March 9, 1972

TO: All Bureau Offices
FROM: Mr. J. Edgar Hoover, Director, FBI
COUNTERINTELLIGENCE PROGRAM
SECURITY MATTER — NEW LEFT

Gump is watching me. I can feel it.

————————

March 27, 1972

TO: All Bureau Offices
FROM: Mr. J. Edgar Hoover, Director, FBI
COUNTERINTELLIGENCE PROGRAM
SECURITY MATTER — NEW LEFT

WHERE ARE YOU, FORREST GUMP!!!!!!!!!

———

April 18, 1972

TO: All Bureau Offices
FROM: Mr. J. Edgar Hoover, Director, FBI
COUNTERINTELLIGENCE PROGRAM
SECURITY MATTER — NEW LEFT

The voices. I can hear them. They're
whispering, "Life is like a box of chocolates."
They're mocking me.

———

April 30, 1972

TO: Mr. J. Edgar Hoover, Director, FBI
FROM: Mr. C. A. Tolson, Associate Director, FBI
COUNTERINTELLIGENCE PROGRAM
SECURITY MATTER — NEW LEFT

J.,

Why aren't you returning my calls? All this
Gump crap is killing our ~~friend~~ ██████ship.
Also, we are going to lose our deposit on
the condo in Florida if we don't move quickly. So
call me as soon as you get this.

———

May 2, 1972

TO: Richard M. Nixon, President of the United
States
FROM: Mr. J. Edgar Hoover, Director, FBI
COUNTERINTELLIGENCE PROGRAM
SECURITY MATTER — NEW LEFT

    I don't get it. I just don't get it. For five
years I've had all of my best people following
Gump night and day. Watching his every move.
Listening to every phone call as he droned on
about Bubba and Jenny and Lieutenant Dan with
that pathetic fake southern accent of his.
    We tried everything. We ███████████████████
██
██
████████████████████████████████ Patrice Lumumba
██
██
Guatemala ███████████████████████████████████████
██
████████████████████████ Stonewall ██████████████
    We even █████████████████████████████████████
██
██████████████████████ Jimi Hendrix █████████████
██
██

But it was all for naught. He's bested us.
He's bested the greatest intelligence agency in
the history of the world. How? HOW?

DAMN YOU, FORREST GUMP! DAMN YOU TO HELL!

May 3, 1972

TO: Richard M. Nixon, President of the United States
FROM: Mr. W. M. Felt, Lead Investigator, COINTELPRO
COUNTERINTELLIGENCE PROGRAM
SECURITY MATTER — NEW LEFT

Mr. President,

The Bureau is mourning the loss of Director Hoover. He was a paragon of integrity and resolve, and he will no doubt be remembered as one of the greatest civil servants in the history of this nation.

Attached you will find a memo addressed to you that he had just finished drafting before he went into cardiac arrest.

The Counterintelligence Program had been monitoring the individual mentioned in the letter, Private Forrest Gump, U.S. Army Special Services, for many years under suspicion of ties to the New Left and Black Extremist groups. Director Hoover, in particular, took an outsized interest in this individual, becoming increasingly obsessed with ensuring Gump's destruction during the last months of his life.

As you know, I have been the Associate Director in charge of the Counterintelligence Program and, more recently, have also led the Bureau's surveillance into possible illegal activities of the Democratic National Committee. I am happy to carry on those duties as you search for a new Director. No doubt they will have big shoes to fill.

In the meantime, we do not believe Private Gump is an imminent threat to national security at this time. However, he is slated for a visit to

the White House next week and we will be on high
alert. I suggest you keep Gump close. Perhaps you
might consider putting him up in the Watergate
Hotel? I have agents stationed all over the
Watergate complex, so we'll be able to keep a
close eye on him there.

————

June 7, 1976

TO: Roderick M. Hills, Chairman, SEC
FROM: Clarence M. Kelley, Director, FBI
SECURITIES FRAUD

Chairman Hills,

I received your request for cooperation in
the investigation into former Army Lieutenant Dan
Taylor, of the Bubba Gump Shrimp Company,
regarding possible insider trading violations
related to his early investments in Apple
Corporation.

I have faxed you Lt. Taylor's criminal
record as well as some documents related to his
repeated refusal to cooperate with previous Bureau
investigations. Pardon the repeated expletives.

What you may also find of interest is a
lengthy file I discovered on his long-time
business partner, Mr. Forrest Gump, who had ties

to extremist groups the Bureau was monitoring
years ago. I will have my office fax you those
documents as well.

————

June 22, 1976

TO: Roderick M. Hills, Chairman, SEC
FROM: Clarence M. Kelley, Director, FBI

    Gump is on the run.

————

June 24, 1976

TO: Roderick M. Hills, Chairman, SEC
FROM: Clarence M. Kelley, Director, FBI

    Never mind, he's just running.

Acknowledgments

Thank you so much for reading my book! I'd love to know what you think. Please leave it a review on Amazon or Goodreads, and for more of my work (as well as random musings about the art of writing), subscribe to my newsletter, Shades of Greaves, at shadesofgreaves.substack.com

This book was a labor of love, and could not have been written without my wife, Cristina, who was a brainstorming partner, shoulder to cry on, and all-around support system. The book also would not have been possible without my fantastic editor, Ginny Hogan, whose edits helped me turn so many half-baked ideas into actual stories, and to Brooks Becker, Lottie Hayes-Clemens, Alison Cnockaert, and Alana McCarthy, who turned a clunky word document into a polished, designed, and illustrated paperback. And, of course, the book would not have been possible without all of the friends, family, and fans who supported the crowdfunding campaign that brought this project to life.

As you're reading this, I encourage you to give all of these people a huge round of applause in your mind (so as not to disturb the other people in the cozy coffee shop I imagine you're in right now). Writing this has been a years-long dream in the making, and I'm so grateful to all of the following supporters:

Gary Almeter

Haldun Anil

Johnathan Appel

Andrea Cabrera

Alex and Brianna Cusson

Milo Feinberg

Rochelle E. Fisher

Will Gaviria

Moose Gibbons

Alex Greaves

Carlos A. Greaves and
Catherine Greaves

Sara Greaves

Christina Jones

Celia Laskowski

Tomo Lazovich

Franco M.

Amanda and Jason Milam

Viveka Mishra

Tito y Yoly Muñoz

Amber Nicholson

Gila Pfeffer

Ivan Ruiz and Myrna Ruiz

Damien Smith

Dusty S.

Leonard Tampkins

Jamie and Adam Vachon

Ari Vogel

David Yatim and Hedwig Wenninger